# my **revisi⏻n** notes

## AQA AS/A-level Year 1

# PHYSICS

Keith Gibbs

**HODDER**
EDUCATION
AN HACHETTE UK COMPANY

Hachette UK's policy is to use papers that are natural, renewable and recyclable products and made from wood grown in sustainable forests. The logging and manufacturing processes are expected to conform to the environmental regulations of the country of origin.

Orders: please contact Bookpoint Ltd, 130 Park Drive, Milton Park, Abingdon, Oxon OX14 4SB. Telephone: (44) 01235 827720. Fax: (44) 01235 400454. Email education@bookpoint.co.uk

Lines are open from 9 a.m. to 5 p.m., Monday to Saturday, with a 24-hour message answering service. You can also order through our website: www.hoddereducation.co.uk

ISBN: 978 1 4718 5470 5

© Keith Gibbs 2016

First published in 2016 by

Hodder Education,
An Hachette UK Company
Carmelite House
50 Victoria Embankment
London EC4Y 0DZ
www.hoddereducation.co.uk

Impression number    10 9 8 7 6 5 4 3 2 1

Year        2020 2019 2018 2017 2016

Cover photo reproduced by permission of kolazig/Fotolia

Typeset by Integra Software Services Pvt. Ltd., Pondicherry, India

Printed in Spain

A catalogue record for this title is available from the British Library.

# Get the most from this book

Everyone has to decide his or her own revision strategy, but it is essential to review your work, learn it and test your understanding. These Revision Notes will help you to do that in a planned way, topic by topic. Use this book as the cornerstone of your revision and don't hesitate to write in it — personalise your notes and check your progress by ticking off each section as you revise.

## Tick to track your progress

Use the revision planner on pages 4 and 5 to plan your revision, topic by topic. Tick each box when you have:
- revised and understood a topic
- tested yourself
- practised the exam questions and gone online to check your answers and complete the quick quizzes

You can also keep track of your revision by ticking off each topic heading in the book. You may find it helpful to add your own notes as you work through each topic.

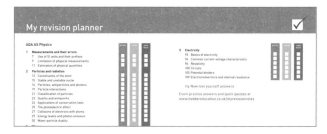

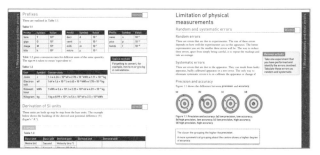

# Features to help you succeed

## Exam tips

Expert tips are given throughout the book to help you polish your exam technique in order to maximise your chances in the exam.

## Typical mistakes

The author identifies the typical mistakes candidates make and explains how you can avoid them.

## Now test yourself

These short, knowledge-based questions provide the first step in testing your learning. Answers are at the back of the book.

## Definitions and key words

Clear, concise definitions of essential key terms are provided where they first appear.

Key words from the specification are highlighted in bold throughout the book.

## Revision activities

These activities will help you to understand each topic in an interactive way.

## Exam practice

Practice exam questions are provided for each topic. Use them to consolidate your revision and practise your exam skills.

## Summaries

The summaries provide a quick-check bullet list for each topic.

## Online

Go online to check your answers to the exam questions and try out the extra quick quizzes at **www.hoddereducation.co.uk/myrevisionnotes**

# My revision planner

## AQA AS Physics

REVISED   TESTED   EXAM READY

Exam practice answers and quick quizzes at **www.hoddereducation.co.uk/myrevisionnotes**

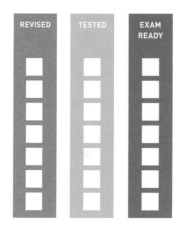

REVISED  TESTED  EXAM READY

**Exam practice answers and quick quizzes at
www.hoddereducation.co.uk/myrevisionnotes**

# Countdown to my exams

## 6–8 weeks to go

- Start by looking at the specification — make sure you know exactly what material you need to revise and the style of the examination. Use the revision planner on pages 4 and 5 to familiarise yourself with the topics.
- Organise your notes, making sure you have covered everything on the specification. The revision planner will help you to group your notes into topics.
- Work out a realistic revision plan that will allow you time for relaxation. Set aside days and times for all the subjects that you need to study, and stick to your timetable.
- Set yourself sensible targets. Break your revision down into focused sessions of around 40 minutes, divided by breaks. These Revision Notes organise the basic facts into short, memorable sections to make revising easier.

REVISED

## 2–6 weeks to go

- Read through the relevant sections of this book and refer to the exam tips, exam summaries, typical mistakes and key terms. Tick off the topics as you feel confident about them. Highlight those topics you find difficult and look at them again in detail.
- Test your understanding of each topic by working through the 'Now test yourself' questions in the book. Look up the answers at the back of the book.
- Make a note of any problem areas as you revise, and ask your teacher to go over these in class.
- Look at past papers. They are one of the best ways to revise and practise your exam skills. Write or prepare planned answers to the exam practice questions provided in this book. Check your answers online and try out the extra quick quizzes at **www.hoddereducation.co.uk/myrevisionnotes**
- Use the revision activities to try out different revision methods. For example, you can make notes using mind maps, spider diagrams or flash cards.
- Track your progress using the revision planner and give yourself a reward when you have achieved your target.

REVISED

## One week to go

- Try to fit in at least one more timed practice of an entire past paper and seek feedback from your teacher, comparing your work closely with the mark scheme.
- Check the revision planner to make sure you haven't missed out any topics. Brush up on any areas of difficulty by talking them over with a friend or getting help from your teacher.
- Attend any revision classes put on by your teacher. Remember, he or she is an expert at preparing people for examinations.

REVISED

## The day before the examination

- Flick through these Revision Notes for useful reminders, for example the exam tips, exam summaries, typical mistakes and key terms.
- Check the time and place of your examination.
- Make sure you have everything you need — extra pens and pencils, tissues, a watch, bottled water, sweets.
- Allow some time to relax and have an early night to ensure you are fresh and alert for the examinations.

REVISED

## My exams

**AS Physics Paper 1**

Date:................................................................

Time:................................................................

Location:..........................................................

**A2 Physics Paper 2**

Date:................................................................

Time:................................................................

Location:..........................................................

# 1 Measurements and their errors

## Use of SI units and their prefixes

### Fundamental (base) units

#### Mass — measured in kilograms

The kilogram (kg) is the mass equal to that of the international prototype kilogram kept at Sevres, France.

#### Length — measured in metres

The metre (m) is the distance travelled by electromagnetic waves in free space in $1/299\,792\,458\,s$.

#### Time — measured in seconds

The second (s) is the duration of $9\,192\,631\,770$ periods of the radiation corresponding to the transition between two hyperfine levels of the ground state of caesium-137 atom.

### Further SI units

#### Electric current — measured in amperes

The ampere (A) is that constant current that, if maintained in two parallel straight conductors of infinite length and of negligible circular cross section placed 1 metre apart in a vacuum, would produce a force between them of $2 \times 10^{-7}\,N$.

#### Temperature — measured in Kelvin

The Kelvin (K) is $1/273.16$ of the thermodynamic temperature of the triple point of water.

#### Amount of substance — measured in moles

The mole (mol) is the amount of substance in a system that contains as many elementary particles as there are in $0.012\,kg$ of carbon-12.

> **Exam tip**
>
> Remember to use the appropriate SI units.

## Prefixes

These are outlined in Table 1.1.

**Table 1.1**

| Prefix | Symbol | Value |
|--------|--------|-------|
| tera | T | $10^{12}$ |
| giga | G | $10^{9}$ |
| mega | M | $10^{6}$ |
| kilo | k | $10^{3}$ |

| Prefix | Symbol | Value |
|--------|--------|-------|
| deci | d | $10^{-1}$ |
| centi | c | $10^{-2}$ |
| milli | m | $10^{-3}$ |
| micro | μ | $10^{-6}$ |

| Prefix | Symbol | Value |
|--------|--------|-------|
| nano | n | $10^{-9}$ |
| pico | p | $10^{-12}$ |
| femto | f | $10^{-15}$ |

Table 1.2 gives conversion rates for different units of the same quantity. The sign ≡ is taken to mean 'equivalent to'.

> **Typical mistake**
>
> Forgetting to convert, for example, mm to m or g to kg in calculations.

**Table 1.2**

| Unit | Symbol | Conversions |
|------|--------|-------------|
| Joule | J | $1\,J \equiv 6.24 \times 10^{18}\,eV \equiv 2.78 \times 10^{-7}\,kWh \equiv 1.11 \times 10^{-17}\,kg$ |
| Electron volt | eV | $1\,eV \equiv 1.6 \times 10^{-19}\,J \equiv 4.45 \times 10^{-26}\,kWh \equiv 1.78 \times 10^{-36}\,kg$ |
| Kilowatt hour | kWh | $1\,kWh \equiv 3.6 \times 10^{6}\,J \equiv 2.25 \times 10^{25}\,eV \equiv 4.01 \times 10^{-11}\,kg$ |
| Kilogram | kg | $1\,kg \equiv 8.99 \times 10^{16}\,J \equiv 5.6 \times 10^{35}\,eV \equiv 2.5 \times 10^{10}\,kWh$ |

## Derivation of SI units

These units are built up step by step from the base units. The example below shows the building of the derived unit potential difference (V) $(kg\,m^2\,s^{-3}\,A^{-1})$.

> **Example**
>
> **Table 1.3**
>
> | Base unit | Base unit | Derived unit | Derived unit | Derived unit |
> |-----------|-----------|--------------|--------------|--------------|
> | Metre (m) | Second | Velocity ($m\,s^{-1}$) | | |
> | Ampere (A) | Second | Charge (C) ($A\,s$) | | |
> | Second (s) | | Velocity | Acceleration ($m\,s^{-2}$) | |
> | Kilogram (kg) | | Acceleration | Force (N) ($kg\,m\,s^{-2}$) | |
> | | Metre | Force | Work (J) ($kg\,m^2\,s^{-2}$) | |
> | | | Work | Charge | Potential difference (V) ($kg\,m^2\,s^{-3}\,A^{-1}$) |

> **Now test yourself**
>
>
> 1 What is the result of multiplying 10 MN by 25 pm? Your answer should include both the numerical answer and the correct unit.
> 2 Using a table like the one above, show the building of the derived unit Pascal (Pa).
>
> Answers on p. 114

# Limitation of physical measurements

## Random and systematic errors

### Random errors

These are errors that are due to experimenter. The size of these errors depends on how well the experimenter can *use* the apparatus. The better experimenter you are the smaller these errors will be. The way to reduce these errors, apart from simply being careful, is to repeat the readings and take an average.

### Systematic errors

These are errors that are due to the apparatus. They can result from faulty apparatus, badly calibrated apparatus or a zero error. The only way to eliminate systematic errors is to re-calibrate the apparatus or change it!

**Revision activity**

Take one experiment that you have performed and identify the errors involved. Tabulate these errors as random and systematic.

### Precision and accuracy

Figure 1.1 shows the difference between **precision** and **accuracy**.

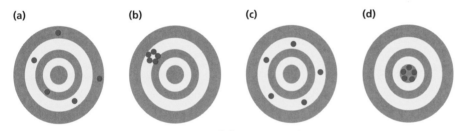

(a)   (b)   (c)   (d)

**Figure 1.1 Precision and accuracy: (a) low precision, low accuracy; (b) high precision, low accuracy; (c) low precision, high accuracy; (d) high precision, high accuracy**

The closer the grouping the higher the **precision**.

A more symmetrical grouping about the centre shows a higher degree of **accuracy**.

Measurements can also be considered in terms of their **repeatability** (whether they can be repeated), their **reproducibility** (whether their values can be reproduced when measured many times) and their **resolution** (an example of resolution would be pixels per $mm^2$ in an image).

### Uncertainty

The uncertainty ($\Delta Q$) in a quantity $Q$ ($Q = a + b$) is:

$$\Delta Q = \Delta a + \Delta b$$

where $\Delta a$ and $\Delta b$ are the uncertainties in the quantities $a$ and $b$. The percentage uncertainty ($\%Q = (\Delta Q/Q) \times 100$) is:

$$\%Q = \%a + \%b$$

If $Q = anb$ (where $n$ can be any number including 1):

$$\Delta Q = b\Delta a + an\Delta b$$

and

$$\%Q = \%a + n\%b$$

Find the maximum possible percentage uncertainty in the measurement of the acceleration of an object that moves at $20 \pm 1 \text{ m s}^{-1}$ in a circle of radius $5 \pm 0.2 \text{ m}$. $(a = v^2/r)$

Answer

$$\%a = (2 \times \%v) + \%r = \left[\left(2 \times \frac{1}{20}\right) + \left(\frac{0.2}{5}\right)\right] \times 100 = 14\%$$

But:

$$a = \frac{20^2}{5} = 80 \text{ m s}^{-2}$$

Therefore the answer for $a$ should be quoted as:

acceleration $(a) = 80 \text{ m s}^{-2} \pm 14\%$

## Uncertainty in graphs

The uncertainty in any point on a graph is shown by the error bars.

Figure 1.2 shows a series or readings of voltage and current for a metal wire. The line of gradient $m$ is the best-fit line to the points where the two extremes, $m_1$ and $m_2$ show the maximum and minimum possible gradients that still lie through the error bars of all the points. The percentage uncertainty in the gradient is given by:

$$\frac{m_1 - m_2}{m} = \left(\frac{\Delta m}{m}\right) \times 100\%$$

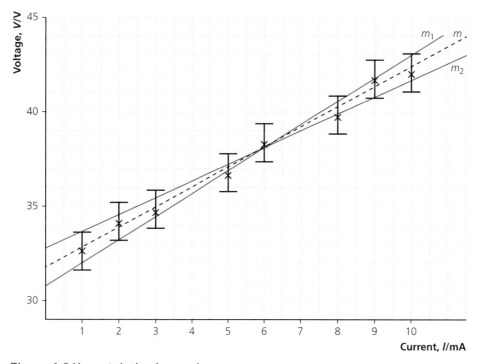

Figure 1.2 Uncertainties in graphs

# Estimation of physical quantities

## Orders of magnitude

REVISED

Physicists use the phrase 'the right order of magnitude' to refer to a number in the right sort of range. For example, finding the time of swing of a 1-metre pendulum as 1.2 s and not 12 s, the specific heat capacity of water as $4500\,\mathrm{J\,kg^{-1}\,K^{-1}}$ and not $45\,000\,\mathrm{J\,kg^{-1}\,K^{-1}}$, or working out that the refractive index of an air–glass interface is 1.4 and not 0.4.

## Estimation of approximate values of physical quantities

REVISED

It is always a good idea to be able to estimate the size of a quantity, so that when you work out a problem or finish an experiment you have a rough idea of what sort of value to expect.

**Exam practice**

1 Using a table similar to Table 1.3 (p. 8) show that the derived unit for resistance (the ohm) can be expressed in SI base units as $\mathrm{kg\,m^2\,A^{-2}\,s^{-3}}$. [3]

2 The derived SI unit for work is:
   A  watt
   B  joule per second
   C  Newton second
   D  joule. [1]

3 The resistance of a 60 cm length of wire is $0.5\,\Omega$ and its diameter 0.3 mm. If the uncertainty in the measurement of its length is 5%, that of the diameter 2% and that of the resistance 8%, calculate the resistivity of the wire and give the percentage accuracy of your answer. [3]

4 The density of a spherical ball of iron is measured by finding its mass and then measuring its diameter. The mass can be measured to $\pm 10\,\mathrm{g}$ and the diameter to $\pm 2\,\mathrm{mm}$. If the mass of the ball is found to be 1.54 kg and the diameter 7.2 cm, which of the following is closest to the correct accuracy for its density?
   A  $\pm 270\,\mathrm{kg\,m^{-3}}$
   B  $\pm 700\,\mathrm{kg\,m^{-3}}$
   C  $\pm 270\,\mathrm{g\,m^{-3}}$
   D  $\pm 700\,\mathrm{g\,m^{-3}}$ [1]

5 Figure 1.3 shows a series of readings of applied force and length for a metal wire.

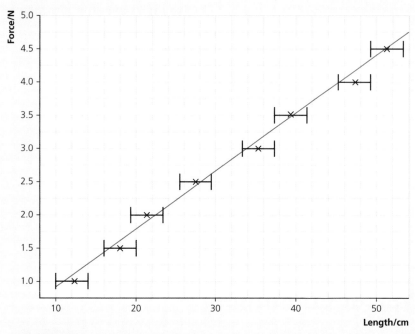

**Figure 1.3** Extension of a metal wire

Use the graph to find:
(a) the value of length when the applied force is zero [3]
(b) the percentage uncertainty in the value of the length of the wire when the applied force is 30 N [2]
(c) the mean value for the gradient of the line [2]
(d) the uncertainty in the value that you calculated. [2]

## Answers and quick quiz 1 online

ONLINE

## Summary

You should now have an understanding of:
● fundamental (base) units — kilogram, metre, second
● how to derive further SI units, such as potential difference, resistance, momentum and pressure
● prefixes — tera, giga, mega, kilo, centi, milli, micro, nano, pico and femto
● how to convert between units
● random and systematic errors — random errors are due to the experimenter and systematic errors are due to the apparatus
● repeatability, reproducibility, resolution and accuracy — precision is shown by a close grouping of results and accuracy by a symmetrical grouping
● uncertainty in measurements — the uncertainty of a compound quantity can be found by adding the uncertainties of its parts, whether fractional or percentage
● uncertainty in graphs — add error bars to points on a graph and then draw the best fit line through the spread of points
● orders of magnitude — the size of a quantity within a factor of ten
● the importance of estimation — the ability to predict the approximate order of magnitude of a quantity

# 2 Particles and radiation

## Constituents of the atom

### Protons, neutrons and electrons

It was the experiments on the scattering of alpha particles by gold nuclei in the early part of the twentieth century that laid the foundation of our modern ideas of the structure of the atom. A simplified diagram of an atom is shown in Figure 2.1.

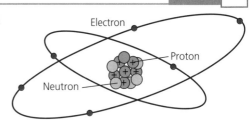

### Charge and mass of protons, neutrons and electrons

**Figure 2.1 Structure of the atom**

Atoms have a diameter of the order of $10^{-8}$ m, and consist of two parts:
- A central heavy nucleus, with diameter of the order of $10^{-15}$ m that contains:
  - **protons** — particles with a unit positive charge of $+1.6 \times 10^{-19}$ C and a mass ($m_p$) of $1.67 \times 10^{-27}$ kg
  - **neutrons** — neutral particles with a mass slightly greater than that of a proton; the neutron mass ($m_N$) is $1.675 \times 10^{-27}$ kg; $m_N = 1.0014 \, m_p$
- **Electrons** orbiting the nucleus. These are particles with a negative charge of $-1.6 \times 10^{-19}$ C, equal and opposite to that of a proton. The mass of the electron ($m_e$) is $9.11 \times 10^{-31}$ kg, or about 1/1836 of that of a proton. The number of these electrons is equal to the number of protons in a non-ionised atom

Note: all figures quoted are for the rest masses of the particles. Relativistic effects will be ignored.

> **Exam tip**
>
> Remember to use the correct SI units.

### Specific charge of nuclei and of ions

A useful quantity is the **specific charge** of a particle. This is defined as follows:

$$\text{specific charge of a particle} = \frac{Q}{m}$$

where $Q$ is the charge on the particle and $m$ is its mass. The units for specific charge are coulombs per kg.

The specific charges of a number of particles are given in Table 2.1.

**Table 2.1 Particles and their specific charges**

| Particle | Specific charge |
|---|---|
| A proton | $\dfrac{+1.6 \times 10^{-19}}{1.67 \times 10^{-27}} = +9.58 \times 10^{7} \, \text{C kg}^{-1}$ |
| An electron | $\dfrac{-1.6 \times 10^{-19}}{9.11 \times 10^{-31}} = -1.76 \times 10^{11} \, \text{C kg}^{-1}$ |
| A nucleus of carbon 12 | $\dfrac{+(12 \times 1.6 \times 10^{-19})}{1.992 \times 10^{-27}} = +9.64 \times 10^{8} \, \text{C kg}^{-1}$ |

## Proton and nucleon number

The **nucleon number** varies from 1 for the simplest form of hydrogen to about 250 for the heaviest elements. The **proton number** varies from 1 to just over 100 for the same range of particles.

> The **proton number** ($Z$) is the number of protons in a nucleus.
>
> The **nucleon number** ($A$) is the total number of neutrons and protons in a nucleus.

## Nuclear notation

The correct way of writing down the structure of a nuclide, showing the proton and nucleon numbers, is shown in Figure 2.2.

## Isotopes

Neon has 10 protons in its nucleus but may occur in a number of different forms with nucleon numbers of 20, 21 and 22, corresponding respectively to 10, 11 and 12 neutrons in the nucleus. These different forms are known as **isotopes** of neon.

> **Isotopes** are different atoms of the same chemical element, i.e. they have the same proton numbers, with different nucleon numbers.

Figure 2.3 shows the three isotopes of hydrogen.

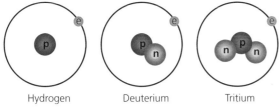

**Figure 2.3 Isotopes of hydrogen**

- The chemical properties of isotopes of the same element are identical.
- Their nuclear properties will be different and some of their physical properties, such as boiling point, are different as well

### Example

Mercury has seven naturally occurring isotopes with nucleon numbers of 196, 198, 199, 200, 201, 202 and 204. The proton number of mercury is 80. How many neutrons are contained in each isotope?

Answer

**neutron number = nucleon number – proton number**

The neutron numbers are 116, 118, 119, 120, 121, 122 and 124.

### Exam tip

The nucleon number was previously called the mass number, while the proton number was known as the atomic number.

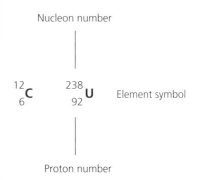

Nucleon number

$^{12}_{6}$C      $^{238}_{92}$U      Element symbol

Proton number

**Figure 2.2 Nuclide notation**

### Typical mistake

Confusing the nucleon and proton number in the nuclide notation.

### Revision activity

Make a table showing the nuclear structure of two isotopes of four different elements.

TESTED

## Now test yourself

1 The proton number of uranium is 92. How many neutrons are there in the following two isotopes of uranium:
   (a) uranium-235 (nucleon number 235)
   (b) uranium-238 (nucleon number 238)
2 What is the nucleon number of the nucleus containing 26 protons and 28 neutrons? (This is an isotope of iron.)

Answers on p. 114

# Stable and unstable nuclei

## The strong nuclear force

REVISED

There are two kinds of particle in the nucleus of an atom — protons, carrying a unit positive charge, and neutrons, which are uncharged. The electrostatic repulsion between all those positively charged protons would tend to blow it apart were it not for the existence of another attractive force between the nucleons. This is known as the **strong nuclear force**.

> The **strong nuclear force** acts between particles in the nucleus and is responsible for the stability of the nucleus.

The strong nuclear force between two nucleons is a short-range force. It is attractive and acts up to a nucleon separation of about 3 fm ($3 \times 10^{-15}$ m). This 'holds the nucleons together' in the nucleus. However, at very small nucleon separations of less than 0.5 fm it becomes repulsive. The repulsive nature at these very small distances keeps the nucleons at a minimum separation.

In small nuclei the strong force from all the nucleons reaches most of the others in the nucleus but for nuclei with more protons and neutrons the balance becomes much finer. The nucleons are not held together so tightly and this can make the nucleus unstable.

> **Exam tip**
>
> The strong nuclear force is very short range, while the electrostatic force affects all the nuclei in the nucleus.

## Alpha and beta emission

REVISED

Radioactive decay, the result of instability in a nucleus, is the emission of particles from the nucleus or a loss of energy from it as electromagnetic radiation.

The two types of particle emitted are the alpha particle (two protons and two neutrons — a helium nucleus) and the beta particle (an energetic electron).

Figure 2.4 shows the changes in nucleon and proton number due to the emission of either an alpha particle or a beta particle.

Example emissions of an alpha and a beta particle, expressed in equation form, are given below,

(a) Alpha emission:

$$^{226}_{88}\text{Ra} \rightarrow {}^{222}_{86}\text{Rn} + {}^{4}_{2}\alpha$$

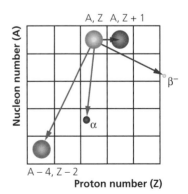

Figure 2.4 Alpha and beta emission

(b) Beta emission:

$$^{90}_{38}Sr \rightarrow ^{90}_{39}Y + ^{0}_{-1}\beta + \bar{\nu}_e$$

Note: the particle $\bar{\nu}_e$ is an **antineutrino**. The existence of **neutrinos** and antineutrinos is necessary to satisfy nuclear conservation laws (p. 22). They are both neutral particles with virtually no mass.

Knowing the true nature of alpha and beta particles, the equations can also be rewritten as:

(a) Alpha emission:

$$^{226}_{88}Ra \rightarrow ^{222}_{86}Rn + ^{4}_{2}He$$

(b) Beta emission:

$$^{90}_{38}Sr \rightarrow ^{90}_{39}Y + ^{0}_{-1}e + \bar{\nu}_e$$

(c) Beta-plus (positron) emission with the electron neutrino:

$$^{30}_{15}P \rightarrow ^{30}_{14}Si + ^{0}_{+1}e + \nu_e$$

> **Exam tip**
>
> Beta emission is the result of neutron decay within the nucleus.

> **Example**
>
> Plutonium-239 decays to form uranium-235.
> (a) Is this by alpha or beta emission?
> (b) Write down the nuclear equation to show this decay.
>
> Answer
>
> (a) alpha emission
> (b) $^{239}_{94}Pu \rightarrow ^{235}_{92}U + ^{4}_{2}He$

## Now test yourself

TESTED

3 Carbon-14 decays by beta emission.
  (a) What is the resulting nuclide?
  (b) Write down the full nuclear equation for this process.
4 Uranium-238 decays to form thorium-234.
  (a) Is this by alpha or beta decay?
  (b) Write down the full nuclear equation for this process.

Answers on p. 114

# Particles, antiparticles and photons

## Antiparticles

REVISED

All particles of matter have a corresponding antiparticle. The first antiparticle to be identified was the anti-electron or **positron**. The mass of the positron is the same as that of an electron (0.51 MeV — p. 21).

Protons, neutrons and neutrinos each have their antiparticle — the antiproton, the antineutron and the antineutrino. The masses of all these antiparticles are the same as those of their corresponding particles.

There is a whole set of antiparticles that 'mirror' the particles that make up our universe. These antiparticles would combine to form a 'new' type of matter known as **antimatter**.

> **Exam tip**
>
> Particles and antiparticles have opposite charges where this is appropriate (proton and electron).

A proton and antiproton collide and annihilate each other.

Calculate the energy produced in (a) MeV and (b) joules. The rest mass of a proton is 938 MeV.

Answer

  energy produced = 2 × 938 MeV = 1876 MeV

  = 1876 × 1.6 × 10⁻¹³ = 3.0 × 10⁻¹⁰ J

# Photon model of electromagnetic radiation

REVISED

All objects at a temperature above absolute zero emit a range of wavelengths but the peak of the energy–radiation curve moves towards the short-wavelength, high-frequency, end as the temperature of the object is increased. For example, a hot piece of metal glows first red, then orange then yellow and finally white as its temperature is increased.

**Typical mistake**

Assuming that if an object, such as a lump of metal, does not glow it is not hot.

More and more energy is emitted as short-wave radiation (Figure 2.5).

The two curves represent objects at two different temperatures. The lower curve is the lower temperature.

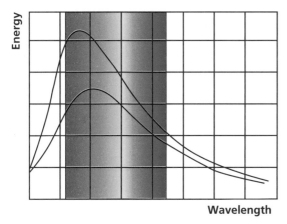

**Figure 2.5 Energy–wavelength graph**

In 1900 the problem of the energy distribution that had been puzzling scientists for some time was solved by Max Planck. He proposed that radiation was emitted not in a continuous stream of energy but in bundles of energy that we now call **photons**.

The energy of a **photon** is given by the formula:

$$\text{photon energy } (E) = hf$$

where $f$ is frequency and $h$ is Planck's constant, with a value of $6.63 \times 10^{-34}$ J s.

Radiation of a higher frequency, and therefore a shorter wavelength, will be composed of photons that have a greater energy.

We can use this idea to calculate the number of photons emitted by a 100 W yellow light per second. (frequency of yellow light = $5 \times 10^{14}$ Hz)

Answer

energy emitted by the light bulb every second = 100 J

energy of each quantum = $hf = 6.63 \times 10^{-34} \times 5 \times 10^{14} = 3.31 \times 10^{-19}$ J

Therefore:

number emitted per second = $\dfrac{100}{3.31 \times 10^{-19}}$ = $3.0 \times 10^{20}$ photons per second

The energy of each photon must be very small otherwise they would hurt when they hit you!

## Now test yourself

TESTED

5 Calculate the energies of a photon of the following wavelengths:
   (a) gamma rays    wavelength $10^{-3}$ nm
   (b) X-rays        wavelength 0.1 nm
   (c) violet light  wavelength 420 nm
   (d) yellow light  wavelength 600 nm
   (e) red light     wavelength 700 nm
   (f) microwaves    wavelength 2 cm
   (g) radio waves   wavelength 254 m

Answer on p. 114

## Particle annihilation

REVISED

When a positron meets an electron the two particles annihilate each other, converting their mass back into energy in the form of electromagnetic radiation (see Figure 2.6). Two gamma rays are needed to conserve momentum. The energy produced in this case is about 1.02 MeV.

A similar event will occur between any particle and its antiparticle.

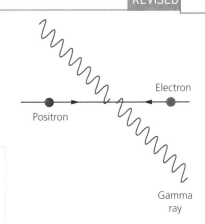

Figure 2.6 Particle–antiparticle annihilation

Example

A proton collides with an antiproton and they annihilate each other. Calculate the energy released in MeV. (rest mass of a proton = 938 MeV; rest mass of an antiproton = 938 MeV)

Answer

energy released = 2 × 938 = 1876 MeV

In high-energy collisions between protons and antiprotons, for example those in the Large Hadron Collider at CERN, the particles annihilate each other. The sum of their mass energy and kinetic energy is converted into radiation and other particles. The initial energy of the proton and antiproton can be as high as 800 GeV ($800 \times 10^3$ MeV).

## Pair production

The reverse of particle annihilation can occur. When a gamma ray passes close to a nucleus it can interact with that nucleus, forming a positron and an electron. This is known as **pair production**. Matter and antimatter have been produced from energy (the gamma ray — Figure 2.7).

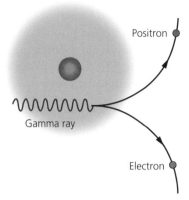

**Figure 2.7 Pair production**

# Particle interactions

There are at present only four certainly known types of force, and these are listed below. The relative importance of each force in an interaction depends on the type of interaction being considered.

- The **gravitational force** acts between all particles with mass and is responsible for holding planets in orbit around the Sun. Range: infinite, varying as $1/d^2$.
- The **electromagnetic force** acts between all charged particles, and is the binding force of atoms and molecules. Range: infinite, varying as $1/d^2$
- The **weak force** is responsible for radioactive decay and the change in quark flavour. It acts between all particles. It is seen in lepton reactions such as the reaction between a neutrino and a muon. Range: about $10^{-3}\,\text{fm}$ ($10^{-18}\,\text{m}$).
- The **strong force** holds neutrons and protons together in a nucleus. It only acts between hadrons since they contain quarks. Range: about $3\,\text{fm}$. Repulsive up to $0.5\,\text{fm}$ and attractive from $0.5\,\text{fm}$ to $3\,\text{fm}$.

## Exchange particles

These fundamental forces can be explained by describing them in terms of **exchange particles**. These are particles that are passed between the two interacting particles and so 'carry' the force between them. These exchange particles are shown in Table 2.2.

**Table 2.2 Exchange particles**

| Force (interaction) | Particle name | Charge |
|---|---|---|
| Electromagnetic | Photon | 0 |
| Strong | Gluon | 0 |
| Gravitational | Graviton | 0 |
| Weak | W+ | +e |
| | W- | -e |
| | Z | 0 |

> **Exam tip**
>
> At the time of writing (2015) the exchange particle for gravitational force, the graviton, has not been discovered.

> **Exam tip**
>
> Remember that in the interaction *both* particles emit a particle or a photon, hence the name — exchange particles.

> **Typical mistake**
>
> Confusing exchange particles with 'actual' particles.

When an electron repels another electron they *both* emit a photon. These photons are 'exchanged' between the two electrons and this 'carries' the force to 'push them apart'. In the weak interaction that governs $\beta^-$ and $\beta^+$ decay, electron–proton collisions and electron capture, the exchange particles are the $W^-$, the $W^+$ and the Z respectively.

# Particle interaction diagrams (Feynman diagrams)

These were developed to provide a clear method of showing the interaction between sub-nuclear particles. They are a way of representing what is happening between the two particles *during* an interaction. (In the following Feynman diagrams time goes from bottom to top.)

Each point where lines come together is called a vertex. At each vertex charge, baryon number and lepton number must be conserved. (For an explanation of these terms see p. 21.)

## Electromagnetic force interaction

Figure 2.8 shows the interaction between two electrons. In classical physics the electrons, both with a negative charge, would repel each other. The diagram shows that this repulsion occurs because of the interchange of photons. Each electron emits a photon, which is then absorbed by the other electron. The photons in the interaction are known as **virtual photons** because they are emitted and absorbed in a time so short that the uncertainty principle is not violated. (To simplify the diagram only one of the virtual photons is shown.)

## Weak force interaction

The weak force interaction in Figure 2.9 shows the emission of a $\beta^-$ in the decay of a free neutron to a proton and an antineutrino. The exchange particle in this interaction is a $W^-$.

The weak force interaction in Figure 2.10 shows the emission of a $\beta^+$ in the decay of a proton to a neutron and an antineutrino. The exchange particle in this interaction is a $W^+$.

## Electron capture

Electron capture is a process in which an electron in the inner shell of an atom is absorbed by the nucleus, changing a nuclear proton to a neutron and simultaneously emitting a neutrino (Figure 2.11).

## Electron–proton collision

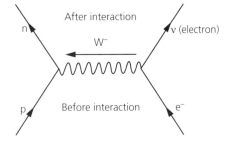

**Figure 2.12 Electron–proton collision**

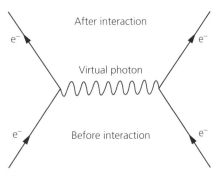

**Figure 2.8 Electron–electron interaction**

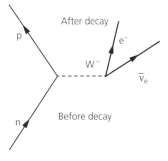

**Figure 2.9 Neutron decay**

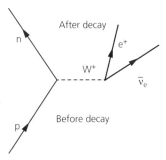

**Figure 2.10 Proton decay**

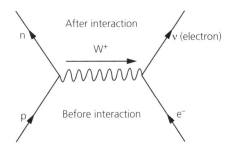

**Figure 2.11 Electron capture**

> **Revision activity**
>
> Make your own Feynman diagrams for some further interactions.

# Classification of particles

## Fundamental particles

The fundamental particles that make up our universe can be divided into three main categories:

- hadrons — these particles 'feel' the strong nuclear interaction (force)
- leptons — these particles 'feel' the weak nuclear interaction
- exchange particles

These three categories are further divided as follows:

- **Hadrons** are composed of two or three quarks:
  - Baryons — protons, neutrons (each composed of three quarks)
  - Mesons — pions, kaons (each composed of two quarks)
  
  (Every particle has its own antiparticle.)
- **Leptons** — electrons, muons, neutrinos — subject to the weak interaction
  
  (Every particle has its own antiparticle.)
- **Exchange particles** — the interactions between particles in the previous two groups are carried by exchange particles (photons, gluons, $W^{\pm}$, Z and gravitons). For more on exchange particles, see p. 19

Leptons and hadrons are summarised in Table 2.3.

> **Typical mistake**
>
> Not remembering to which category a particle belongs.

**Table 2.3 Leptons and hadrons**

| Particle | Symbol | Rest energy/ MeV | Charge/e | Lifetime |
|---|---|---|---|---|
| **Leptons** | | | | |
| Electron | e | 0.511 | −1 | >$4.6 \times 10^{26}$ years |
| Neutrino | $v_e$ and $v_\mu$ | Very small | 0 | Stable |
| Muon | μ | 105.7 | −1 | $2.2 \times 10^{-6}$ s |
| **Hadrons** | | | | |
| Mesons | | | | |
| Pion | $\pi^+$ | 139.6 | +1 | $2.6 \times 10^{-8}$ s |
| | $\pi^0$ | 135.0 | 0 | $0.8 \times 10^{-16}$ s |
| Kaon | $K^-$ | 495 | −1 | $1.24 \times 10^{-8}$ s |
| Baryons | | | | |
| Proton | p | 938.3 | +1 | >$1 \times 10^{29}$ years |
| Neutron (free) | n | 939.6 | 0 | 650 s |

## Lepton number

All leptons have a 'property' called a **lepton number**, $L_e$ (= 1) for electrons and electron-neutrinos and $L_\mu$ (= 1) for muons and muon-neutrinos. Their antiparticles have lepton numbers of −1 for both positrons and antineutrinos.

## Baryon number

All baryons and antibaryons are given a **baryon number**. This is +1 for baryons and −1 for anti-baryons.

To account for the strange behaviour of some hadrons a 'new' property of hadrons was proposed, called **strangeness** (S). Protons and neutrons have a strangeness of zero, while kaons have a strangeness of +1 or −1.

**Exam tip**

Remember that although mesons are hadrons they are not baryons and so their baryon number is 0.

| Particle | S | Particle | S | Particle | S |
|---|---|---|---|---|---|
| n | 0 | $e^+$ and $e^-$ | 0 | $\pi$ | 0 |
| p | 0 | $\nu$ | 0 | $K^+$ | +1 |

## Conservation in particle interactions

REVISED

- The total charge is always conserved in a particle interaction.
- The total baryon number is always conserved in a particle interaction.
- The total lepton number is always conserved in a particle interaction.
- Strangeness is conserved in strong interactions but not in weak interactions

### Examples

1   Show that the quantum number conservation laws for charge and lepton number are obeyed in the following reaction:

$n \rightarrow p^+ + e^- + \bar{\nu}_e$

Answer

|  | n | $\rightarrow$ | $p^+$ | + | $e^-$ | + | $\bar{\nu}_e$ |
|---|---|---|---|---|---|---|---|
| Charge | 0 |  | +1 |  | −1 |  | 0 |
| Lepton number ($L_e$) | 0 |  | 0 |  | 1 |  | −1 |
| Strangeness (S) | 0 |  | 0 |  | 0 |  | 0 |

Therefore the conservations laws are followed and the interaction will take place.

2   Show that the following reaction does not obey all the quantum number conservation laws and will therefore not happen:

$n + K^+ \rightarrow \pi^0 + \pi^+$

Answer

|  | n | + | $K^+$ | $\rightarrow$ | $\pi^0$ | + | $\pi^+$ |
|---|---|---|---|---|---|---|---|
| Charge | 0 |  | +1 |  | 0 |  | +1 |
| Baryon number | 1 |  | 0 |  | 0 |  | 0 |
| Strangeness (S) | 0 |  | +1 |  | 0 |  | 0 |

Therefore the conservations laws are not followed and the interaction will not take place.

### Now test yourself

TESTED

6   Show that the quantum number conservation laws for charge and lepton number are obeyed in the following reaction:

$\mu^+ \rightarrow e^+ + \bar{\nu}_\mu + \bar{\nu}_e$

Answer on p. 114

Exam practice answers and quick quizzes at **www.hoddereducation.co.uk/myrevisionnotes**

# Quarks and antiquarks

All hadrons are composed of particles called **quarks**. These were finally discovered in 1975 by the bombardment of protons by very high-energy electrons.

At the present time (2015) quarks are thought to be the fundamental particles of matter. Quarks have fractional electric charge compared with the charge on the electron of −e.

The existence of quarks was confirmed by high-energy electron scattering from the nucleons. There are actually six quarks and their antiquarks, but we will only consider three types here (together with their antiquarks):
- the up quark (u)
- the down quark (d)
- strange quark (s)

See Figure 2.13.

Note: the full list of quarks is up, down, strange, charm, bottom and top.

**Figure 2.13 Quarks**

## Properties of quarks                                        REVISED

Table 2.4 shows the properties of up, down and strange quarks.

**Table 2.4 Quark properties**

| Quark | Symbol | Charge | Baryon number | Strangeness |
|-------|--------|--------|---------------|-------------|
| Up | u | $+\frac{2}{3}$ | $\frac{1}{3}$ | 0 |
| Down | d | $-\frac{1}{3}$ | $\frac{1}{3}$ | 0 |
| Strange | s | $-\frac{1}{3}$ | $\frac{1}{3}$ | −1 |

## Combinations of quarks                                      REVISED

Note: the colours of the quarks in the following diagrams are simply to make them distinguishable.

### Baryons

Baryons are formed from combinations of three quarks or antiquarks (Figure 2.14).

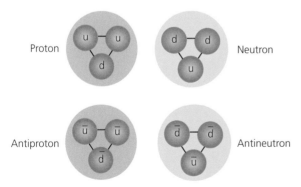

**Figure 2.14 Quark structure of baryons**

## Mesons

Mesons are formed from combinations of two quarks or antiquarks (Figure 2.15).

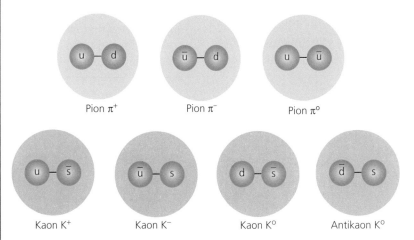

Figure 2.15 Quark structure of mesons

# Applications of conservation laws

## Quark model of beta emission

REVISED

The quark nature of the proton and neutron can be used to explain beta emission:

$\beta^+$ emission: $p \rightarrow n + \beta^+ + \nu$

Quark version:

$\beta^+$ emission (proton decay): uud $\rightarrow$ ddu + 0 + 0

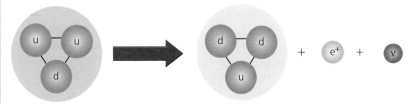

Figure 2.16 Quark model of $\beta^+$ emission

In proton decay an up quark changes into a down quark.

$\beta^-$ emission: $n \rightarrow p + \beta^- + \bar{\nu}$

Quark version:

$\beta^-$ emission (neutron decay): ddu $\rightarrow$ uud + 0 + 0

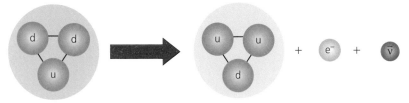

Figure 2.17 Quark model of $\beta^-$ emission

When a neutron decays by $\beta^-$ emission a down quark changes into an up quark.

# The photoelectric effect

## Photon explanation of threshold frequency

Figure 2.18 shows a charged clean zinc plate fitted to the top of a gold leaf electroscope. The plate may be positive or negative and various forms of radiation can be shone on it.

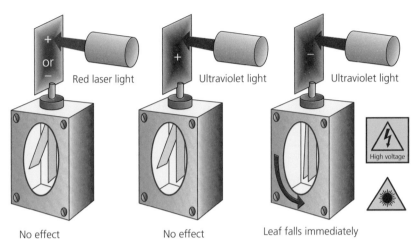

No effect          No effect          Leaf falls immediately

**Figure 2.18** The photoelectric effect

If the plate is positively charged no radiation has any effect. However, if the plate is given a negative charge to start with there *is* a difference. Using the laser-emitting red light has no effect, but when ultraviolet light is shone on the plate the electroscope is discharged and the leaf falls immediately. No effect can be produced with radiation of longer wavelength (lower frequency and smaller energy) no matter how long the radiation is shone on the plate.

When the ultraviolet radiation fall on the plate:
- no electrons are emitted from the plate if it is positive
- the number of electrons emitted per second depends on the intensity of the incident radiation
- the energy of the electrons depends on the frequency of the incident radiation
- there is a minimum frequency $(f_0)$ below which no electrons are emitted no matter how long radiation fell on the surface

These results show that:
- The **threshold frequency** is the minimum frequency $(f_0)$ that will cause electron emission from a given material. Photons with a lower frequency will never cause electron emission.
- The free electrons are held in the metal in a 'hole' in the electric field; this is called a **potential well**. Energy has to be supplied to them to enable them to escape from the surface (Figure 2.19).

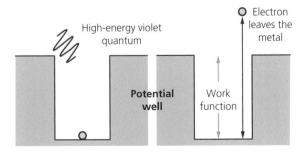

**Figure 2.19** The potential well

If radiation with a frequency above that of the threshold frequency is shone on a metal plate electrons are emitted spontaneously. One quantum of radiation (a photon) of a high enough frequency has enough energy to 'kick the electron out' in one go.

**The photoelectric effect is very good evidence for the particle nature of electromagnetic waves.**

The amount of energy needed to just release a photoelectron is known as the **work function** ($\varphi$) for the metal. This can be expressed in terms of the threshold frequency ($f_0$).

**work function ($\varphi$) = $hf_0$**

where $h$ is Planck's constant ($6.63 \times 10^{-34}$ Js)

**Example**

If the work function of silver is $7.6 \times 10^{-19}$ J, calculate the threshold frequency for a clean silver surface.

Answer

$$\text{threshold frequency } (f_0) = \frac{W}{h} = \frac{7.6 \times 10^{-19}}{6.63 \times 10^{-34}} = 1.15 \times 10^{15} \text{ Hz}$$

(This is in the ultraviolet region of the spectrum.)

## Einstein's photoelectric equation                                 REVISED

If a quantum of radiation with an energy ($hf$) greater than the work function $\varphi$, and therefore a frequency greater than $f_0$, falls on a surface an electron will escape from the surface and be emitted with some residual kinetic energy ($E_k$).

The energy of the incident quantum ($hf$) is the sum of the work function of the metal ($\varphi = hf_0$) and the maximum kinetic energy of the electron ($E_k$) (Figure 2.20). This is expressed by Einstein's photoelectric equation:

$$hf = \varphi + E_k = hf_0 + E_k$$

## Stopping potential                               REVISED

If we put a collecting electrode in front of the emitting surface in a vacuum we can detect the photoelectrons as a small current. If the collecting electrode is made slightly negative compared with the emitting surface the electrons will find it difficult to get to it and electrons will only do that if their energy is greater than the 'height' of the potential barrier.

Electrons will be only detected if $E_k > eV$ where $V$ is the potential difference between the plate and the emitting surface.

If $V$ is increased so that no more electrons can reach the detector, this value for the potential is called the **stopping potential** for that surface and radiation.

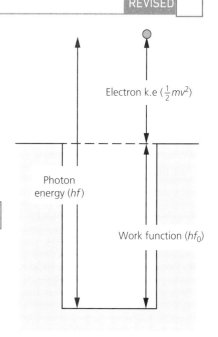

Figure 2.20 Einstein's photoelectric equation

Calculate the maximum kinetic energy of an electron that is emitted from a magnesium surface when light of wavelength 180 nm falls on it. (work function for magnesium = $5.9 \times 10^{-19}$ J)

Answer

frequency of incident radiation $= \dfrac{3 \times 10^8}{180 \times 10^{-9}} = 1.67 \times 10^{15}$

kinetic energy $= hf - hf_0 = hf - \varphi$

$= (6.63 \times 10^{-34} \times 1.67 \times 10^{15}) - 5.9 \times 10^{-19} = 1.11 \times 10^{-18} - 5.9 \times 10^{-19} = 5.17 \times 10^{-19}$ J

## Now test yourself

7 Light with a wavelength of 150 nm is needed to cause photoelectric emission from the surface of a piece of metal. Calculate the work function for that metal.
8 Radiation of wavelength 120 nm falls on a zinc plate. Electrons are emitted with a maximum energy of $6.6 \times 10^{-19}$ J.
  Calculate:
  (a) the energy of a quantum of the incident radiation
  (b) the work function for zinc
  (c) the threshold frequency for zinc
  (speed of light, $c = 3 \times 10^8$ m s$^{-1}$; Planck's constant, $h = 6.63 \times 10^{-34}$ J s)

Answers on p. 114

**Exam tip**

Do not forget to convert nm to m when using the photoelectric equation.

**Revision activity**

Summarise the main features of photoelectric emission in a mind map or table and emphasise what it shows about the nature of radiation.

# Collisions of electrons with atoms

## Ionisation and excitation

A simplified version of an energy level diagram for electrons in an atom is shown in Figure 2.21. The electrons are spread through the energy levels. No electron can have an energy state between the levels.

In hydrogen there is just one orbiting electron. The electron is usually in its unexcited or **ground state** — level 1 (Figure 2.22(a)).

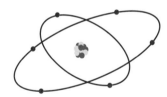

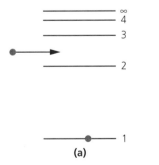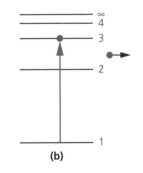

**Figure 2.22 Excitation**

If energy is put into the atom in the form of radiant energy or by an inelastic collision with a charged particle, an electron is raised to a higher energy level and is said to be **excited** and in an **excited state**.

In Figure 2.22(b) the electron has been raised to level 3 and the colliding electron has lost some energy.

**Figure 2.21 Electrons in an atom**

If the collision with an incoming electron is sufficiently violent an electron within the atom can be given enough energy to raise it to the level marked with an infinity symbol. This level is called the **ionisation level**.

If the energy input is great enough to raise it above that level the electron will escape from the atom altogether. This is called **ionisation** (Figure 2.23).

The removal of one (or more) electrons will leave the atom with a net positive charge — it has become a positive ion.

The energy required to ionise a hydrogen atom is $21.8 \times 10^{-19}$ J. This assumes that the electron starts off in its ground state.

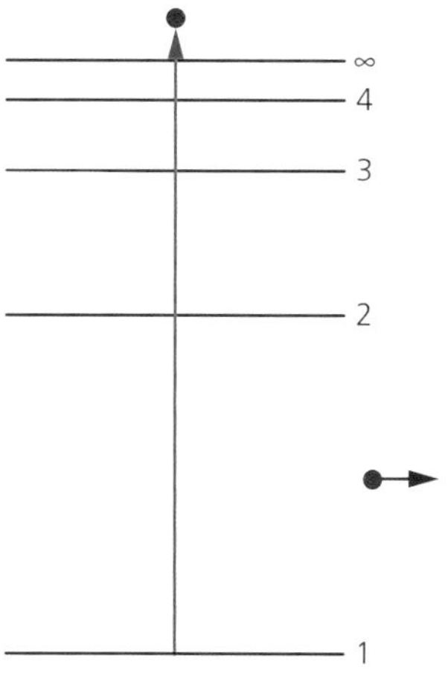

## The fluorescent lamp

The fluorescent lamp is a sealed glass tube containing a gas such as mercury at low pressure. A filament in the tube produces electrons by thermionic emission and these move at speed through the tube due to a large electric field between the two electrodes.

Collisions between these electrons and the mercury atoms excite atoms of the gas. Transitions within the mercury atoms give out radiation, which is mostly in the ultraviolet region of the spectrum, and finally these ultraviolet photons interact with the phosphor on the glass walls of the tube, producing visible light.

Figure 2.23 Ionisation

## The electron volt

REVISED

Joules are very large units when subatomic particles are considered. A much smaller unit known as the **electron volt** is used when stating their energies.

> An **electron volt** (eV) is the energy gained by an electron when it is accelerated through a potential difference of 1 volt.
>
> **1 eV = 1 V × 1.6 × 10⁻¹⁹ C = 1.6 × 10⁻¹⁹ J**

Yellow light, wavelength 600 nm, has a frequency of $5 \times 10^{14}$ Hz and so the energy of a photon of yellow light is:

energy = $hf$ = $6.63 \times 10^{-34} \times 5 \times 10^{14}$ = $3.31 \times 10^{-19}$ J

which, when expressed in electron volts, is:

$$\frac{3.31 \times 10^{-19}}{1.6 \times 10^{-19}} = 2.07 \, eV$$

Larger energies can be expressed in keV ($10^3$ eV) and MeV ($10^6$ eV).

### Example

Calculate the energy of a photon of ultraviolet light with a wavelength of 100 nm in both (a) joules and (b) electron volts. (Planck's constant, $h = 6.63 \times 10^{-34}$ J s; speed of light, $c = 3 \times 10^8$ m s⁻¹; 1 eV = $1.6 \times 10^{-19}$ J)

#### Answer

frequency, $f = \dfrac{c}{\lambda} = \dfrac{3 \times 10^8}{100 \times 10^{-9}} = 3 \times 10^{15}$ Hz

(a)  $E = hf = 6.63 \times 10^{-34} \times 3 \times 10^{15} = 1.99 \times 10^{-18}$ J

(b)  $E = \dfrac{1.99 \times 10^{-18}}{1.6 \times 10^{-19}} = 12.4 \, eV$

# Energy levels and photon emission

## Atomic line spectra

When light from an incandescent monatomic gas is viewed with a spectroscope a spectrum similar to the one shown on Figure 2.24 is seen.

**Figure 2.24 Atomic line spectrum**

The spectrum shows a series of bright lines, which is very good evidence for the structure of the atom. The simplest spectrum is that of hydrogen. When an electron drops from one level to another a quantum of radiant energy known as a photon is emitted and this gives a line in the hydrogen spectrum.

The greater the energy transition the higher the frequency of the emitted radiation. The separation of the energy levels in the atom can be predicted from the wavelengths, and hence frequencies, of the radiation emitted (Figure 2.25).

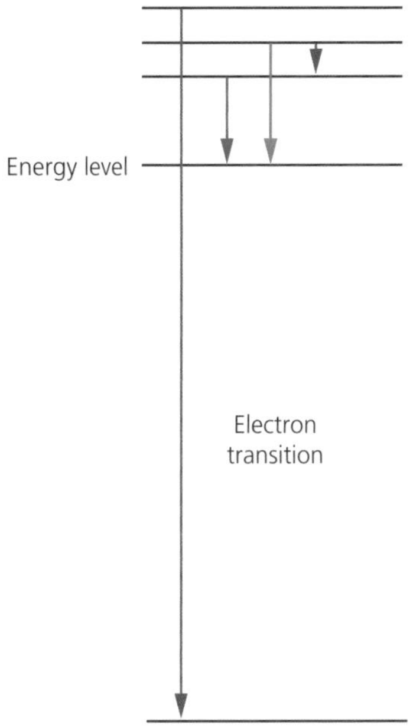

Energy level

Electron transition

**Figure 2.25 Electron transitions**

## The spectrum of atomic hydrogen

The energy levels in atomic hydrogen are shown in Figure 2.26.

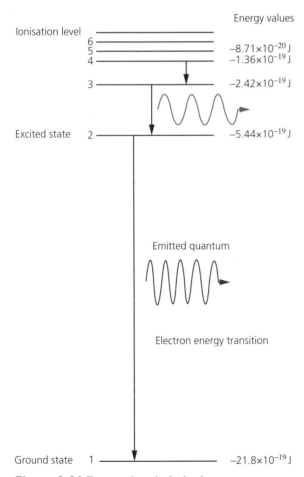

**Figure 2.26 Energy levels in hydrogen**

When an electron falls from one level to another energy is emitted in the form of a photon of radiation. The energy of this photon, and therefore its frequency and wavelength, is determined by the difference in energy between the two levels.

$$\text{photon energy} = hf$$

The frequency ($f$) of the photon emitted is related to the difference between the two levels ($E_1 - E_2$) by the equation:

$$hf = E_1 - E_2$$

### Example

Calculate the frequency of a photon produced by an electron transition between level 4 and level 2 in the hydrogen atom. (Planck's constant, $h = 6.63 \times 10^{-34}$ J s)

Answer

$E_1 - E_2 = (5.44 - 1.36) \times 10^{-19}$ J $= 4.08 \times 10^{-19}$ J

$f = \dfrac{E_1 - E_2}{h} = \dfrac{4.08 \times 10^{-19}}{6.63 \times 10^{-34}} = 6.15 \times 10^{14}$ Hz

Radiation of this frequency has a wavelength of $\dfrac{c}{f} = 488$ nm.

### Now test yourself

TESTED

9 Calculate the frequency and wavelength of a photon of radiation emitted due to an electron transition in a hydrogen atom between level 2 and level 1 (use Figure 2.26).

Answer on p. 114

# Wave–particle duality

## Electron diffraction

REVISED

If electrons have wave properties they should show the characteristics of waves such as interference and diffraction. The fact that electron diffraction can be observed suggests that particles do have wave properties.

The diagrams in Figure 2.27 show the effects produced by electron diffraction through a thin graphite sheet.

**(a)** Low accelerating voltage      **(b)** High accelerating voltage

**Figure 2.27 Electron diffraction rings**

**Electron diffraction is very good evidence for the wave nature of particles.**

If the accelerating voltage is increased the energy and momentum of the electrons is increased, and the diameter of a given ring gets less, showing a smaller angle of diffraction.

The wave theory of particles suggests that this is because the electrons' wavelength has also decreased. This is exactly similar to the observation that blue light with a short wavelength and high energy is diffracted through a smaller angle than low-energy red light.

**Revision activity**

Make a simple mind map of electron diffraction, showing in which part of the experiment the electrons' wave properties predominate and where their particle properties predominate.

## The de Broglie wavelength

REVISED

Louis de Broglie proposed that a particle of mass $m$ travelling with a velocity $v$ would have a wavelength $\lambda$ given by the equation:

$$\text{wavelength, } \lambda = \frac{h}{mv}$$

where $h$ is Planck's constant and $mv$ is the momentum of the particle. The intensity of the wave at any point represents the probability of the particle being at that point.

An electron accelerated through a potential difference of $V$ volts will gain electrical energy $(E = eV)$ and hence kinetic energy $\frac{1}{2}mv^2$. The wavelength associated with the electron at that energy is given by:

$$\text{electron wavelength, } \lambda = \frac{12.27 \times 10^{-10}}{\sqrt{V}}$$

An electron of high energy has a smaller wavelength than one of low energy.

---

**Example 1**

Calculate the wavelength associated with an electron that has been accelerated through a potential difference of 5 kV.

Answer

$$\text{wavelength} = \frac{12.27 \times 10^{-10}}{\sqrt{V}} = \frac{12.27 \times 10^{-10}}{\sqrt{5000}}$$

$$= 1.74 \times 10^{-11} \text{ m} = 0.017 \text{ nm}$$

(Compare this value with that for yellow light — about 600 nm.)

---

Strangely, whether a particle behaved like a particle or a wave seemed to be influenced by the nature of the experiment used.

---

**Example 2**

Calculate the wavelength of an electron emitted by a nucleus at 0.9 c. (mass of an electron travelling at this speed = $2.4 \times 9 \times 10^{-31}$ kg at this speed; $c = 3 \times 10^8$ ms$^{-1}$)

Answer

$$\text{wavelength, } \lambda = \frac{6.63 \times 10^{-34}}{2.4 \times 9 \times 10^{-31} \times 3 \times 10^8} = 1.0 \times 10^{-12} \text{ m}$$

---

2 Particles and radiation

## Now test yourself

10 Calculate the wavelength associated with a proton moving at $10^7\,\mathrm{m\,s^{-1}}$. (mass of a proton = $1.67 \times 10^{-27}\,\mathrm{kg}$; Planck's constant = $6.63 \times 10^{-34}\,\mathrm{J\,s}$)

Answer on p. 114

## Exam practice

Use the following values where needed:

speed of electromagnetic radiation in free space, $c = 3 \times 10^8\,\mathrm{m\,s^{-1}}$

Planck's constant, $h = 6.63 \times 10^{-34}\,\mathrm{J\,s}$

1 The following equation represents the alpha emission from a uranium nucleus:

$$^{235}_{92}\mathrm{U} \rightarrow\, ^{a}_{b}\mathrm{Th} +\, ^{4}_{2}\alpha$$

  (a) What are the numbers $a$ and $b$? [2]

  (b) What do they represent? [2]

2 Which of the following combinations of alpha ($\alpha$) and beta ($\beta$) particles can $^{214}_{84}\mathrm{Po}$ emit and become another isotope of polonium?

  A  $\alpha$ and $4\beta$       B  $\alpha$ and $2\beta$       C  $\alpha$ and $\beta$       D  $2\alpha$ and $\beta$ [1]

3 (a) What are the four properties conserved in particle interactions? [4]

  (b) Explain whether the following reaction obeys nuclear conservation laws. [2]

$$\mathrm{p} + \mathrm{n} \rightarrow \mathrm{p} + \mu^{+} + \mu^{-}$$

4 This question is about quarks.

  (a) How many quarks make up (i) a baryon, (ii) a meson? [2]

  (b) Write down the quark version of the decay of a neutron by beta-minus emission. [2]

5 The quark composition of an antiproton is:

  A  uud       B  ddu       C  $\bar{\mathrm{u}}\bar{\mathrm{u}}\bar{\mathrm{d}}$       D  $\mathrm{u}\bar{\mathrm{u}}\mathrm{d}$ [1]

6 'Photon' is the name given to:

  A  a unit of energy

  B  an electron emitted from a metal surface by incident radiation

  C  a positively charged atomic particle

  D  a quantum of electromagnetic radiation [1]

7 (a) (i) What is meant by the 'work function' in the photoelectric effect? [2]

      (ii) Which electrons are emitted in the photoelectric effect? [1]

  (b) Radiation of wavelength 180 nm ejects electrons from a potassium plate whose work function is 2.0 eV.

      (i) What is the maximum energy of the emitted electrons? [3]

      (ii) What is the maximum wavelength that will cause electron emission? [2]

8 An electron makes a transition from level 4 (energy −0.85 eV) to level 3 (energy −1.5 eV) in a hydrogen atom.

  (a) Calculate the wavelength of the radiation emitted. [2]

  (b) Suggest in which region of the electromagnetic spectrum this radiation lies. [1]

9 The wavelength of radiation emitted when an electron in an atom makes a transition from an energy state $E_1$ to one of energy $E_2$ is:

  A  $\dfrac{hc}{E_2} - \dfrac{hc}{E_1}$

  B  $\dfrac{E_1}{hc} - \dfrac{E_2}{hc}$

  C  $\dfrac{hc}{E_1} - \dfrac{hc}{E_2}$

  D  $\dfrac{hc}{E_2 - E_1}$ [1]

10 In an electron beam experiment the wavelength of an electron moving at $4.7 \times 10^6 \, \text{m s}^{-1}$ was found to be 0.155 nm.

   (a) What value does this give for the rest mass of the electron? (At this speed relativistic effects can be ignored.)      [2]

   (b) The beam of electrons is now diffracted using a graphite sheet. What effect would a decrease of electron accelerating voltage have on the diameter of the diffraction rings?      [1]

   (c) What does the size of the diffraction rings and the wavelength of the electrons show about the spacing of the atoms in the graphite sheet?      [2]

## Answers and quick quiz 2 online

ONLINE

## Summary

You should now have an understanding of:

- structure of the atom — atoms are composed of a nucleus of neutrons and protons with a cloud of electrons orbiting it
- stable and unstable nuclei — some nuclei are unstable and will lose energy by the emission of a particle (alpha and/or beta) or electromagnetic radiation (a gamma ray)
- particles, antiparticles and photons — all particles have their corresponding antiparticle; Planck's constant ($h$) is used to find the energy of a quantum of radiation
- particle interactions — there are four fundamental forces (gravity, electromagnetic, weak and strong), each carried by its own exchange particle
- classification of particles into hadrons (baryons and mesons) and leptons
- quarks and antiquarks — the fundamental 'building blocks' of hadrons; there are three types of quark — up, down and strange

- conservation laws — charge, baryon number, lepton number and strangeness are conserved in all nuclear interactions
- the photoelectric effect — the spontaneous emission of electrons from a surface due to incident radiation if its frequency is high enough
- collisions of electrons with atoms – ionisation occurs when an electron is removed from an atom
- an electron volt (eV) as a small unit of energy
- energy levels and photon emission — when an electron 'falls' from one energy level to another radiation is emitted; the frequency of this depends on the size of the energy transition
- wave–particle duality — particles can behave like waves and waves can behave like particles

# 3 Waves

## Progressive waves

A progressive wave motion transmits energy from the source through a material or a vacuum without transferring matter. Wave motion can occur in many forms, such as water waves, sound waves, radio waves, light waves and mechanical waves.

### Waves: basic properties

REVISED

Waves are produced by the oscillation of particles or electric and magnetic fields. They are defined by the following set of basic properties:

- **Wavelength ($\lambda$)** is the distance between any two successive corresponding points on the wave, for example between two maxima or two minima.
- **Displacement (y)** is the distance from the mean, central, undisturbed position at any point on the wave.
- **Amplitude (a)** is the maximum displacement from zero to a crest or a trough.
- **Frequency (f)** is the number of vibrations per second made by the wave. Frequency is measured in Hertz (Hz). A frequency of 1 Hz is a rate of vibration of one oscillation per second. High frequencies are measured in kilohertz (kHz) (1 kHz = 1000 Hz) and megahertz (MHz) (1 MHz = 1 000 000 Hz).
- **Period (T)** is the time taken for one complete oscillation ($T = 1/f$).
- **Phase ($\varepsilon$)** is a term related to the displacement at zero time (see p. 35).
- **Path difference** is the difference in distance travelled by two waves from their respective sources to a common point.
- **Speed (c)** is a measure of how quickly energy is transmitted from place to place by the wave motion.

**wave speed (c) = frequency (f) × wavelength ($\lambda$)**

> **Typical mistake**
>
> Taking a wavelength to be the distance along the wave from crest to trough and not crest to crest.

> **Example**
>
> If a note played on a guitar has a frequency of 440 Hz, what is its wavelength? (speed of sound in air = 330 m s$^{-1}$)
>
> Answer
> $$\text{wavelength} = \frac{\text{velocity}}{\text{frequency}} = 0.75\,\text{m}$$

> **Typical mistake**
>
> Taking the amplitude to be the distance from a trough to a crest and not from the 'axis' to a crest.

### Now test yourself

TESTED

1. There are two radio stations broadcasting on the FM radio band. One has a frequency of 101.7 MHz and the other a frequency of 100 MHz. (speed of radio waves = 3 × 10$^8$ m s$^{-1}$)
   What is the wavelength of the radio waves from the station with the shortest wavelength?
2. Explain why an astronaut on the surface of the Moon would be able to see a spacecraft descending towards the lunar surface but would not be able to hear the sound of the rocket engines. (Assume that they have a microphone fitted to the outside of their space helmet.)

Answers on p. 114

## Phase and phase difference

The **phase** of a wave is related to the displacement of a specific point (say a crest) on the wave at zero time. The **phase difference** between two waves is the difference between the positions of the crests on the two waves.

When the positions of the crests and troughs of two waves coincide the waves are in phase. When the crests of one wave coincide with the troughs of the other the waves are out of phase (Figure 3.1). In this case the phase difference between the two waves is $\pi$ radians, or 180°. Waves with a different phase difference would show a different shift along the time axis.

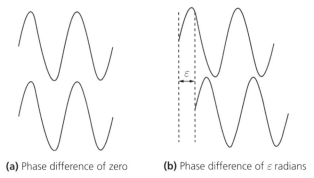

**(a)** Phase difference of zero          **(b)** Phase difference of $\varepsilon$ radians

**Figure 3.1 Phase and phase difference**

# Longitudinal and transverse waves

## Types of wave

Wave motion occurs as one of two types: **longitudinal** and **transverse**.

### Longitudinal waves

In a longitudinal wave (Figure 3.2) the oscillation is along the direction of propagation of the wave, for example sound waves and some mechanical waves.

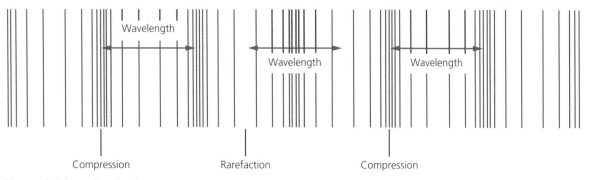

Wavelength          Wavelength          Wavelength

Compression          Rarefaction          Compression

**Figure 3.2 Longitudinal waves**

In a longitudinal wave the particles of the material through which the wave is travelling move from side to side along the wave direction as the wave passes by. This oscillatory movement produces places of low pressure (**rarefaction**) and places of high pressure (**compression**). For this reason a longitudinal wave is sometimes called a pressure wave.

## Transverse waves

In a transverse wave (Figure 3.3) the oscillations are at right angles to the direction of propagation of the wave, for example water waves, most electromagnetic waves and some mechanical waves.

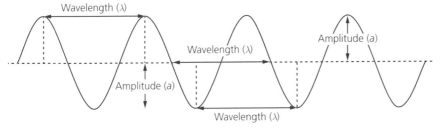

**Figure 3.3 Transverse waves**

# Polarisation

REVISED

A wave in which the plane of vibration is constantly changing is called an **unpolarised** wave. When the vibrations of a transverse wave are in one plane only then the wave is said to be **polarised** (Figure 3.4).

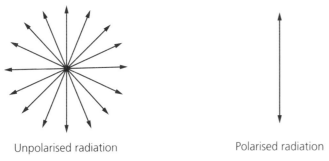

Unpolarised radiation          Polarised radiation

**Figure 3.4 Polarisation**

It is important to realise that transverse waves can be polarised while longitudinal waves cannot. Therefore if a set of waves can be polarised it is very good evidence that these waves are transverse. In Figure 3.5 it is clear that oscillations along the line of propagation will be unaffected by the polariser.

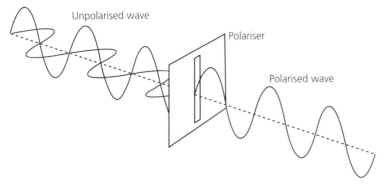

**Figure 3.5 Action of a polariser**

All electromagnetic waves travel at the same speed in a vacuum.

## Applications of polarisation

The uses of polarisation include polarising glasses for viewing 3D films, LCD displays, photographic filters, stress analysis investigation using transparent plastic specimens and 'Polaroid' sunglasses, which reduce the glare from reflected sunlight. This last effect is due to the polarisation of reflected light from a surface.

Polarisation is also important for the transmission and reception of TV signals. The transmitting aerial and the receiving aerial must be aligned in the same direction for optimum signal reception.

> **Revision activity**
>
> Make a table to show which types of waves are transverse and which are longitudinal.

### Now test yourself

TESTED

3 (a) Draw a diagram to show the relative alignment direction for rod-type TV transmitting and receiving aerials.
   (b) What would happen to the received signal as the receiving aerial was slowly rotated about an axis parallel to the direction of propagation of the incoming signal?

Answers on p. 114

# Principle of superposition of waves and formation of stationary waves

## Principle of superposition

REVISED

Unlike particles, waves can pass through each other when then overlap.

> The **principle of superposition** states that when two waves meet, the resulting displacement is the vector sum of the displacements due to each pulse at that point.

## Formation of stationary waves

REVISED

A **stationary wave**, or standing wave, is one in which the amplitude varies from place to place along the wave. Figure 3.6 shows a stationary wave. The amplitude at point 1 is $a_1$, that at point 2 is $a_2$ and that at point 3 is $a_3$. The displacement ($y$) at these points varies with time.

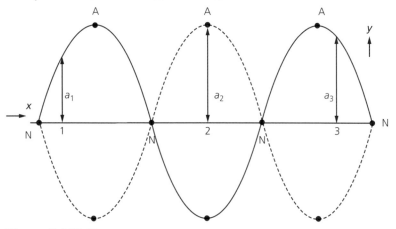

**Figure 3.6 Stationary waves**

Note that there are places where the amplitude is zero and, halfway between, places where the amplitude is a maximum; these are known as **nodes** (labelled N) and **antinodes** (labelled A) respectively.

> **Any stationary wave can be formed by the addition of two travelling waves moving in opposite directions.**

A string is fixed between two points. If the centre of the string is plucked vibrations move out in opposite directions along the string. This causes a transverse wave to travel along the string. The pulses travel outwards along the string and when they reach each end of the string they are reflected.

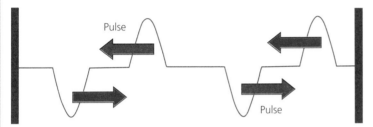

**Figure 3.7 Pulses moving along a string**

The two travelling waves then interfere with each other to produce a standing wave in the string. In the fundamental mode of vibration there are points of no vibration, or nodes, at each end of the string and a point of maximum vibration, or antinode, at the centre.

Notice that there is a phase change when the pulse reflects at each end of the string.

The frequency of the standing wave on a string depends on the length of the string ($L$), its tension ($T$) and the mass per unit length of the string ($\mu$).

For the first harmonic the frequency is given by the formula:

$$\text{frequency, } f = \frac{1}{2L}\sqrt{\frac{T}{\mu}}$$

The first three harmonics for a vibrating string are shown in Figure 3.8.

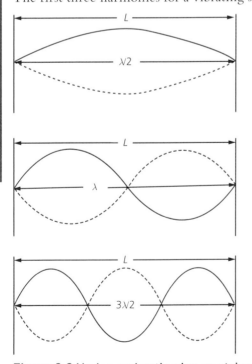

**Figure 3.8 Nodes and antinodes on strings**

Exam practice answers and quick quizzes at **www.hoddereducation.co.uk/myrevisionnotes**

Stationary waves can be formed on strings, as on a guitar or cello, and also using microwaves and sound.

**Example 1**

A stretched string is plucked at the centre and then lightly touched one quarter of the way from one end. Draw the resulting wave that is formed on the string.

*Answer*

When it is lightly touched a node will be produced at that point. The resulting waveform is shown in Figure 3.9.

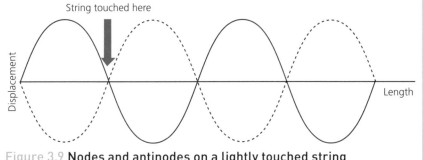

Figure 3.9 **Nodes and antinodes on a lightly touched string**

**Example 2**

A 70 cm long stretched string is plucked so that it vibrates in its second harmonic mode. If the tension in the string is 200 N and the mass per unit length is 1.2 g what note will be heard?

*Answer*

$$\text{frequency, } f = \frac{1}{L}\sqrt{\frac{T}{\mu}}$$

$$= (1/0.7)\sqrt{(200/1.2 \times 10^{-3})} = 583\,\text{Hz}$$

Note the use of the formula for the second harmonic.

## Now test yourself

TESTED ☐

4  What is the distance between adjacent nodes on a standing wave in terms of the wavelength of the standing wave?
5  Why must there always be nodes at the end of a standing wave on a stretched string?
6  A motorist drives along a motorway at a steady speed of 30 m s⁻¹ between two cities listening to the car radio. As she travels along she notices that the radio signal varies in strength, 5 s elapsing between successive maxima. Explain this effect and calculate the wavelength of the radio signal to which she is tuned.

Answers on p. 114

## Required practical 1

### Standing waves on a stretched string

This can be demonstrated by fixing one end of a string to a vibration generator and passing the other end over a bench pulley with a weight fixed to the lower end. When the vibration generator is connected to a signal generator it will vibrate the string. Adjusting the tension and the length of the string and the driving frequency of the signal generator will give standing waves on the string.

# Interference

## Phase difference

When two waves meet at a point the resulting disturbance depends on the amplitudes of both waves at that point. This will depend on the **phase difference** between them. The formation of this disturbance is due to the superposition of the two waves and is called interference.

### Coherent and incoherent sources

Two separate light sources, such as two light bulbs, cannot be used as sources for a static interference pattern because although they may be monochromatic the light from them is emitted in a random series of pulses. The phase difference that exists between one pair of pulses may well be quite different from that between the next pair of pulses (Figure 3.10).

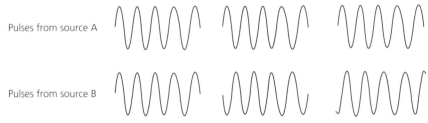

Pulses from source A

Pulses from source B

**Figure 3.10 Coherent and incoherent sources**

An interference pattern still occurs but it changes so rapidly that you get the impression of uniform illumination.

> Sources with synchronised phase changes between them are called **coherent sources** and those with random phase changes are called **incoherent sources**.

If the crest of one wave meets the crest of the other the waves are said to be in phase and the resulting intensity will be large. This is known as **constructive interference**. If the crest of one wave meets the trough of the other (and the waves are of equal amplitude) they are said to be out of phase by $\pi$ and the resulting intensity will be zero. This is known as **destructive interference**.

There will be many intermediate conditions between these two extremes that will give a small variation in intensity.

This phase difference can be produced by allowing the two sets of waves to travel different distances. This difference in distance of travel is called the **path difference** between the two waves.

The diagrams in Figure 3.11 show two waves of equal amplitude with different phase and path differences between them. The first pair have a phase difference of zero and a path difference of a whole number of wavelengths, including zero. This gives constructive interference. The second pair have a phase difference of $\pi$ or 180° and a path difference of an odd number of half-wavelengths, giving destructive interference.

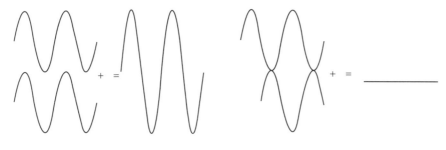

**(a)** Constructive interference                    **(b)** Destructive interference

**Figure 3.11 Constructive and destructive interference**

To obtain a static interference pattern at a point (that is, one that is constant with time) we must have:

● two sources of the same wavelength, and
● two sources that have a constant phase difference between them.

This condition is met by two speakers connected to a signal generator because the sound waves that they emit are continuous — there are no breaks in the waves.

## The laser — coherent light and safety

The problem of coherence of a source is overcome by using a laser. This emits a continuous beam of coherent light, with no abrupt phase changes (Figure 3.12).

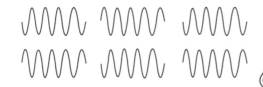

Pulses from source A

Pulses from source B

Laser light

**Figure 3.12 Light waves emitted by a laser**

Care must be taken when using lasers to avoid eye damage. The major problem with a laser is the power density. Light from a 100 W light bulb diverges and so the power density at a distance of 2 m from the source is $2 \, \text{W} \, \text{m}^{-2}$. However a laser beam diverges very little. It is about 2 mm in diameter at a distance of 2 m from a 1 mW laser and so the power density here can be as high as $1.25 \times 10^4 \, \text{W} \, \text{m}^{-2}$.

## Two-source interference systems

A static interference pattern can be obtained using a single source and splitting the beam in two, as in the double-slit method. Light from a narrow single source (S) falls on two parallel slits ($S_1$ and $S_2$). This effectively gives two coherent sources since any phase changes in one source will also occur in the other (Figure 3.13).

Two sources, $S_1$ and $S_2$, emit waves of equal wavelength and these waves meet at a point P on a screen. In Figure 3.14(a) the path difference is 0, producing constructive interference. In Figure 3.14(b) it is half a wavelength and so destructive interference results.

The resulting interference pattern and the fringes formed are shown in Figure 3.15.

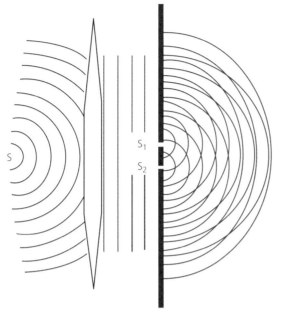

Figure 3.13 A double-slit interference system

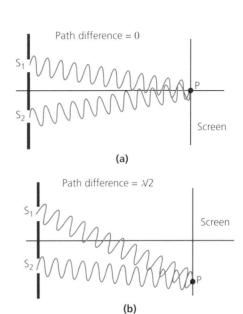

Figure 3.14 Double-slit interference

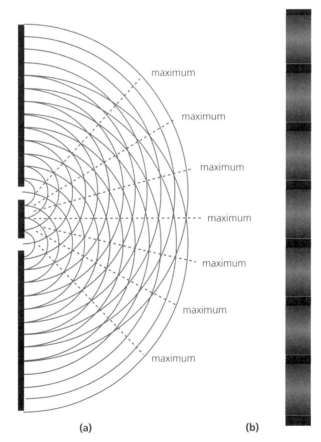

Figure 3.15 Interference pattern and fringes

The fringe spacing (or fringe width) for light of wavelength $\lambda$ is given by the formula:

$$\text{fringe spacing, } w = \frac{\lambda D}{s}$$

where $s$ is the slit spacing and $D$ is the distance of the double slits from the screen.

**Revision activity**

Draw a full-size interference pattern with wavelength of 1 cm and plot the points of constructive and destructive interference.

Calculate the fringe spacing for light of wavelength 600 nm in a double-slit experiment where the double slits are separated by 0.8 mm and the screen is placed 75 cm from them.

Answer

fringe width $(w) = \dfrac{\lambda D}{d} = \dfrac{600 \times 10^{-9} \times 0.75}{0.80 \times 10^{-3}} = 5.6 \times 10^{-4}\,\text{m} = 0.56\,\text{mm}$

## Now test yourself

7  Light of wavelength 600 nm falls on a pair of double slits that are 0.5 mm apart. Calculate:
   (a)  the fringe separation on a screen 90 cm away from the double slits
   (b)  the distance and direction that the screen has to be moved to get the same fringe separation with light of wavelength 500 nm
8  Calculate the wavelength of the light that will give an interference pattern with a fringe width of 4.5 mm on a screen 4 m from a pair of slits with a slit separation of 0.6 mm.

Answers on p. 114

### Required practical 2(i)

### Young's double-slit experiment

The interference of light can be observed using a blackened glass slide on which two fine slits have been engraved parallel to each other and less than a millimetre apart. When the slide is illuminated with monochromatic light a series of fringes will be seen on a screen placed on the other side of the slide from the source. Moving the screen away from the slits will increase the fringe width, as will the use of light of a longer wavelength.

# Diffraction

## Basic principles

When a wave hits an obstacle it does not simply go straight past, but bends round the obstacle. The same type of effect occurs at a hole — the waves spread out the other side of the hole. This phenomenon is known as **diffraction**.

Diffraction effects (Figure 3.16):
● are greater for waves of long wavelength
● are greater for small holes

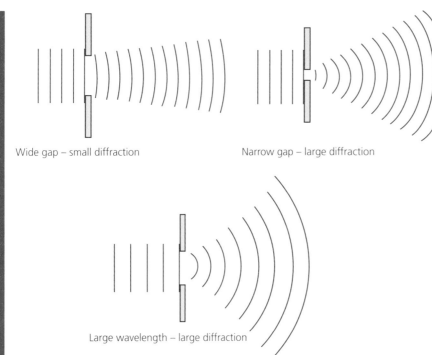

Wide gap – small diffraction

Narrow gap – large diffraction

Large wavelength – large diffraction

**Figure 3.16 Diffraction effects**

## Appearance of the diffraction pattern from a single slit

REVISED

When light passes through a single slit diffraction occurs. The variation of intensity with angle of diffraction ($\theta$) is shown in Figure 3.17.

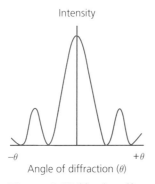

**Figure 3.17 Single-slit diffraction**

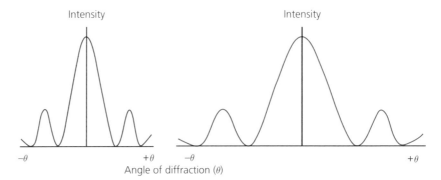

**Figure 3.18 Diffraction and wavelength**

Figure 3.18 shows the effect of a change of wavelength on the diffraction pattern.

**Blue light — short wavelength, giving a narrow diffraction pattern.**

**Red light — long wavelength, giving a broad diffraction pattern.**

If the slit is narrowed the diffraction pattern will become broader for a given wavelength, and it will narrow if the slit is made wider.

If white light is used, a spectrum is formed at each maximum in the diffraction pattern.

9   Why is the diffraction of light much more difficult to observe than the diffraction of microwaves?
10  Can diffraction occur with longitudinal waves as well as with transverse waves?

Answers on p. 114

# The diffraction grating

REVISED

If a number of parallel, narrow slits are made the result is known as a diffraction grating (Figure 3.19). Those in use in schools have typically between 80 and 300 slits per mm. The distance between the centres of adjacent slits is called the **grating spacing** ($d$). If there are 100 slits per mm the width of one slit is 0.01 mm, or $10^{-5}$ m.

The diffracted images produced by diffraction gratings are both sharper and more intense than those produced by a single slit. The intensity in any given direction is the sum of those due to each slit (Figure 3.19).

The slits of a diffraction grating are usually called lines.

## Formula for a diffraction grating

When a parallel beam of light falls on a diffraction grating a number of diffraction maxima are formed. These are formed at angles of $\theta$ to the normal of the grating. The formula for these maxima is:

**diffraction grating maximum, $n\lambda = d\sin\theta$**

where $n = 0, 1, 2, 3\ldots$

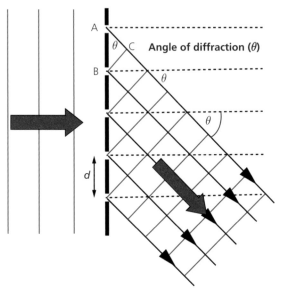

**Figure 3.19 Diffraction grating**

The number $n$ is known as the **order of the spectrum** so that, for example, a first-order spectrum is formed for $n = 1$, and so on. If light of a single wavelength, such as that from a laser, is used, then a series of sharp maxima occur — one maximum to each order of the spectrum. A white light source gives a series of spectra with the light of the shortest wavelength having the smallest angle of diffraction.

The number of orders of spectra visible with a given grating depends on the grating spacing, with more spectra being visible with coarser gratings. This is because the maximum angle of diffraction is 90° and therefore the maximum value for sin $\theta = 1$.

> **Exam tip**
>
> The number of lines per metre on a diffraction grating is the inverse of the grating spacing.

### Example

Calculate the wavelength of the monochromatic light where the second-order image is diffracted through an angle of 25° using a diffraction grating with 300 lines per millimetre.

Answer

grating spacing, $d = \dfrac{10^{-3}}{300\,\text{m}} = 3.3 \times 10^{-6}\,\text{m}$

wavelength, $\lambda = \dfrac{d\sin 25}{2} = \dfrac{3.3 \times 10^{-6} \times 0.42}{2} = 6.97 \times 10^{-7}\,\text{m} = 697\,\text{nm}$

> **Typical mistake**
>
> Forgetting that the diffraction occurs on both sides of the axis of the system.

### Now test yourself

TESTED ☐

11  A diffraction grating has 250 lines per mm. Calculate:
   (a) the angle of diffraction for the first order image for light of wavelength 550 nm
   (b) the highest order possible with this grating at this wavelength
   (c) the number of images of the source
12  How could you tell the difference between a CD and a DVD simply by looking at the diffraction pattern produced by a white light source? Explain your answer.

Answers on p. 114

## Applications of diffraction gratings

Diffraction gratings are very useful tools for the study of spectra. They are often used to determine the composition of an incandescent source and are particularly useful in the analysis of the material of stars. Diffraction gratings are cheaper and easier to use than glass prisms and the spectra produced can be made large by increasing the number of lines per metre.

**Using a diffraction grating to observe a spectrum**

The grating is illuminated with light from a discharge lamp incident at right angles. Light is diffracted from all the slits and the resulting waves interfere with each other to give maxima and minima. The angle of diffraction for each maximum and minimum depends on the wavelength of the light.

# Refraction at a plane surface

When light passes from one medium to another of different refractive index its speed changes (Figure 3.20). This change of speed depends on the refractive index of the two materials. It moves more slowly in a material of higher refractive index than it does in a material of low refractive index. This means that it will refract at a boundary between two media of different refractive index.

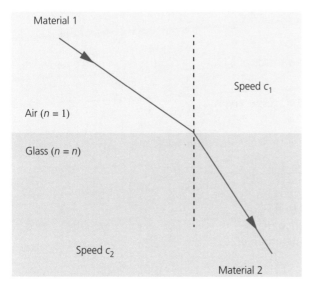

Figure 3.20 Refraction and change of speed

refractive index, $n$ of material $2 = \dfrac{c_1}{c_2}$

**Example**

A beam of light passes from air (refractive index 1.00) into diamond (refractive index 2.42), the speed of light in air being $3.0 \times 10^8\,\text{ms}^{-1}$. Calculate the speed of light in diamond.

Answer

$$\text{speed of light in diamond} = \frac{3 \times 10^8}{2.42} = 1.24 \times 10^8\,\text{ms}^{-1}$$

# Refraction at a boundary between two different substances

The change of speed of a beam of light passing from material 1 to material 2 causes the light to refract. The amount of refraction obeys Snell's law of refraction (Figure 3.21).

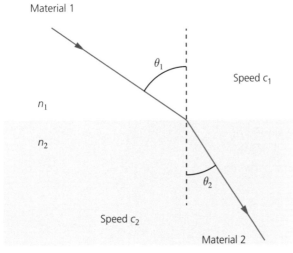

**Figure 3.21 Refraction at a boundary**

If the absolute refractive indices of the materials are $n_1$ and $n_2$ respectively, according to Snell's law:

$$n_1 \sin \theta_1 = n_2 \sin \theta_2$$

**Example**

A beam of light passes from water (refractive index 1.33 ($n_1$)) into diamond (refractive index 2.42 ($n_2$)). If the angle of incidence ($\theta_1$) in water at the water–diamond boundary is 35°, calculate the angle of refraction ($\theta_2$) in the diamond.

Answer

Using:

$$n_1 \sin \theta_1 = n_2 \sin \theta_2$$

$$\sin \theta_2 = \sin \theta_1 \frac{n_1}{n_2} = \sin 35 \frac{1.33}{2.42} = 0.574 \times 0.55 = 0.32$$

Therefore:

angle of refraction ($\theta_2$) = 18.4°

**Exam tip**

The absolute refractive index of a material is its refractive index compared with a vacuum and is the value usually quoted simply as the refractive index.

## Now test yourself

13 A beam of light travelling in glycerol passes into a diamond (refractive index 2.42). Calculate the refractive index of glycerol. The angle of incidence in glycerol is 35° and the angle of refraction in diamond is 20.4°.

Answer on p. 114

## Total internal reflection

REVISED

When light passes from a material such as water into one of lower refractive index such as air there is a maximum angle of incidence in the water that will give a refracted beam in the air, that is, the angle of refraction is 90°. The angle of incidence in the material of higher refractive index corresponding to an angle of refraction of 90° in the material of lower refractive index is known as the **critical angle**, $c$ (Figure 3.22(a)).

If this angle of incidence is exceeded, *all* the light is reflected back into the material of higher refractive index. This is called **total internal reflection** (Figure 3.22(b)) and the normal laws of reflection are obeyed.

$$\sin \theta_c = \frac{n_2}{n_1}$$

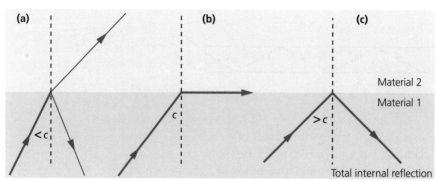

Figure 3.22 The critical angle and total internal reflection

### Exam tip

Total internal reflection only occurs when the light travelling in one material meets a boundary with a material that has a lower refractive index.

### Example

The refractive indices from air to glass and from air to water are 1.50 and 1.33 respectively. Calculate the critical angle for a water–glass surface.

#### Answer

The refractive index for light passing from water to glass [$_w n_g$] is given by:

$$_w n_g = \frac{n_g}{n_w} = \frac{1.5}{1.33} = 1.13$$

Therefore the critical angle (c) can be found from:

$$_w n_g = \frac{1}{\sin c}$$

And so:

$$\sin c = \frac{1}{1.13} = 0.89$$

Therefore, $c = 62.9°$

## Now test yourself

14 Calculate the critical angle for a water–diamond interface if the refractive indices are 1.33 and 2.42 respectively.

15 Show that it is impossible for a beam of light to enter one face of a cubical glass block and leave by the adjacent face. (refractive index of the glass = 1.5)

Answers on p. 114

## Fibre optics

An important application of total internal reflection is in fibre optics. Light is shone along a thin glass fibre and if it hits the glass–air boundary at more than the critical angle it reflects along inside the fibre. These fibres are normally around $125\,\mu m$ ($0.125\,mm$) in diameter (similar to that of a human hair). The core diameter (see later) is around $50\,\mu m$.

The transmission of light down a glass fibre is of enormous importance in communications. Glass fibres are cheap, light in weight compared with copper wire and light can be modulated to carry an enormous amount of information. Figure 3.23 shows the situation for a single glass fibre in air.

**Figure 3.23 Single glass fibre**

Figure 3.24 shows the situation for a single glass fibre with a layer of glass cladding surrounding it. The cladding has a refractive index ($n_1$) significantly greater than air but slightly less than the refractive index of the core of the fibre ($n_2$).

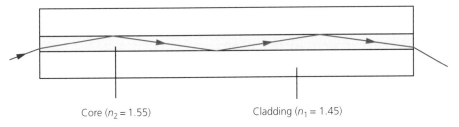

Core ($n_2 = 1.55$)          Cladding ($n_1 = 1.45$)

**Figure 3.24 Single glass fibre with cladding**

The refractive indices from air to the glass of the core and from air to the glass of the cladding are 1.55 and 1.45 respectively. Calculate the critical angle for a water–glass surface.

Answer

The refractive index for light passing from the core to the cladding is:

$$\frac{n_{CORE}}{n_{CLADDING}} = \frac{1.55}{1.45} = 1.069$$

Therefore, the critical angle, $c$, can be found from:

$$_{CORE}n_{CLADDING} = \frac{1}{\sin c}$$

So:

$$\sin c = \frac{1}{1.069} = 0.935$$

Therefore, $c = 69.3°$

## Material dispersion

If a pulse of white light is sent down a fibre with a single layer of cladding **material dispersion** occurs, with different wavelengths taking different times to travel down the fibre. This is because of the different refractive indices of the core for different wavelengths of light. As a result, the pulse spreads and the effect is known as **pulse broadening**.

## Modal dispersion

Another problem is the different time of transmission between rays that make different angles with the axis of the fibre. This is known as **modal dispersion** (Figure 3.25) and can be reduced by cladding the fibre. The greater critical angle when cladding is used means that only rays of light that have a large angle of incidence with the 'walls' of the fibre, and so make a small angle with the axis of the fibre, will be transmitted along it. Other light will refract out of the fibre. This reduces the difference in time of transmission and so the spread of information with time is also reduced.

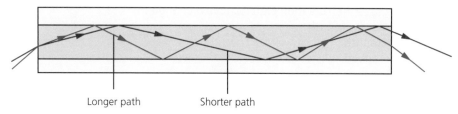

Longer path        Shorter path

**Figure 3.25 The effect of modal dispersion**

The distance that information can be sent down the fibre will be limited both by absorption in the glass of the fibre and by the effects of dispersion if light that is not truly monochromatic is used.

## Now test yourself

TESTED

16 Explain briefly why the use of non-monochromatic light is a problem for the transmission of data along an optical fibre.

Answer on p. 114

## Exam practice

Take the velocity of light in free space to be $3 \times 10^8 \, \text{m s}^{-1}$ where needed.

1 A cello D string has a length of 70 cm and a first harmonic of frequency 73.3 Hz.
   (a) What is the frequency of the second harmonic? [3]
   (b) Where would the cellist have to touch the string to produce this harmonic? [1]
   (c) Calculate the tension in the cello string. [3]
   (mass per unit length = $1.5 \times 10^{-3} \, \text{kg m}^{-1}$)

2 A stretched wire with its ends firmly clamped has a first harmonic of frequency 1000 Hz. What will be the frequency of the first harmonic if the tension of the wire is increased by 2%?
   A  980 Hz
   B  1040 Hz
   C  1020 Hz
   D  1000 Hz [1]

3 (a) Why can't you get a static interference pattern with two light bulbs, while it is possible with two loudspeakers? [2]
   (b) A Young's double-slit experiment is carried out using green light. Describe and explain what will happen to the interference fringes produced if:
     (i)   red light is used instead [1]
     (ii)  blue light is used instead [1]
     (iii) the two slits are moved closer together [1]
     (iv) the two slits are moved further apart [1]
     (v)  white light is used [1]
     (vi) one of the slits is covered up [2]
     (vii) the slits are made narrower. [1]

4 Light from a fluorescent lamp is found to consist of only two wavelengths, 450 nm and light of a longer wavelength. When the light is passed through a given diffraction grating it is found that the third order for the shorter wavelength has the same diffracted angle as the second order for the longer wavelength. Calculate:
   (a) the wavelength of the light with the longer wavelength [3]
   (b) the grating spacing if the angle of diffraction in this case is 20°. [2]

5 Water waves of wavelength 4 m meet a narrow entrance to a harbour. If the entrance is 10 m wide calculate the separation between the central maximum and the first minimum on the beach if the distance from the harbour mouth to the beach is 250 m. [2]

6 A beam of light of wavelength 600 nm hits a glass–air interface at an angle of 40°. If the velocity of light in glass is $2 \times 10^8 \, \text{m s}^{-1}$ find:
   (a) the angle of refraction [2]
   (b) the wavelength of the light in the glass. [2]
   (c) A thin layer of glass of refractive index 1.45 is now added to the original glass surface. Calculate the critical angle for the interface between the two pieces of glass. [3]

7 When visible light passes from air into glass the radiation experiences a change in:
   A  frequency but not in speed and not in wavelength
   B  frequency and speed but not in wavelength
   C  wavelength and frequency but not in speed
   D  wavelength and speed but not in frequency. [1]

8 Explain carefully the effect on the spectrum observed by a plane transmission diffraction grating if the ruled face is presented to the incident light rather than the un-ruled face. [2]

### Answers and quick quiz 3 online

ONLINE

## Summary

You should now have an understanding of:

- progressive waves and stationary waves — waves are formed by oscillations of particles or fields
- how longitudinal waves show oscillations along the direction of wave propagation while transverse waves show oscillations at right angles to the direction of wave propagation
- the principle of wave superposition — the formation of points of no vibration (nodes) and points of maximum vibration (antinodes) on a stretched string
- formation of stationary waves by two travelling waves moving 'through' each other in opposite directions and combining
- interference — the overlapping a two systems of waves giving a pattern showing maxima and minima
- double-slit interference — this gives fringes of one colour using monochromatic light and a series of spectra using white light
- diffraction — this is the spreading of waves through a hole or round an obstacle; it is greater for small obstacles and holes and for long-wavelength waves.
- the use of diffraction grating to give finer and brighter spectra
- refraction of light at a plane surface, producing a change in direction of the refracted light; the speed in a material of high refractive index is less than that in a material of low refractive index
- total internal reflection — this only occurs when light moving in one medium meets a boundary with one with a lower refractive index
- fibre optics — the transmission of light and/ or microwaves along a glass fibre; cladding is used to reduce both material and modal dispersion

# 4 Mechanics and materials

## Scalars and vectors

The quantities measured in physics can be divided into two groups, **scalars** and **vectors**.

> **Scalars** are quantities that have magnitude (size) only. Examples of scalars are length, speed, mass, density, energy, power, temperature, charge and potential difference.
>
> **Vectors** are quantities that have direction as well as magnitude. Examples of vectors are displacement, force, torque, velocity, acceleration, momentum and electric current.

Scalars can be added together by simple arithmetic but when two or more vectors are added together their direction must be taken into account as well.

A vector can be represented by a line, the length of the line being the magnitude of the vector and the direction of the line the direction of the vector.

## Addition of vectors REVISED

When two or more vectors are added the resulting sum of the vectors is called the **resultant vector** or simply the **resultant**.

### Vectors acting in the same line

Two or more vectors acting in the same direction can be added as if they were scalars. For example the sum, or resultant, of the three forces shown in Figure 4.1(a) is 100 N acting right to the left while in Figure 4.1(b) it is 700 N left to right.

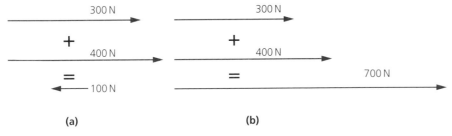

**(a)**                    **(b)**

**Figure 4.1** Vectors acting in the same line

### Vectors acting in different directions

If the two vectors acting at a point are not acting along the same line the resultant can be found by either using a scale diagram or by calculation. The vectors are drawn nose to tail and the resultant closes the triangle. (Note: calculations will be limited to two vectors at right angles (Figure 4.2(a)).

Exam practice answers and quick quizzes at **www.hoddereducation.co.uk/myrevisionnotes**

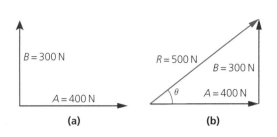

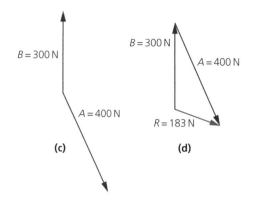

**Figure 4.2** Vectors acting at an angle

### Examples

**Finding the resultant using a scale diagram**

Using the same magnitude for the two vectors as those already considered we draw a scale diagram in both magnitude and direction. The resultant, **R** (= 500 N in this case) is the vector that closes the triangle (Figure 4.2b)

The direction of the resultant can be found by measuring angle $\theta$. In this case $\theta = 37°$.

**Finding the resultant by calculation**

The resultant of the two vectors can also be found by calculation.

$$\text{resultant, } R = \sqrt{400^2 + 300^2} = \sqrt{250\,000} = 500\,\text{N}$$

The direction of $R$ can be found from:

$$\tan \theta = \frac{300}{400} = 0.75$$

So, $\theta = 36.9°$

> **Exam tip**
>
> Notice that the original two vectors (shown blue in Figure 4.2) follow each other round the triangle (nose to tail) to give the **resultant**, the red vector (**R**), and that this resultant acts in the opposite direction round the triangle.

> **Exam tip**
>
> Always choose a sensible scale when drawing scale diagrams of vectors.

An example of two vectors not acting at right angles to each other is shown in Figure 4.2(c) and Figure 4.2(d).

## Now test yourself

TESTED ☐

1 An aircraft is flying on an initial bearing of 0° at 350 m s⁻¹ with a wind blowing west to east at 50 m s⁻¹. Find the true speed of the plane and the direction in which it travels. You should use both the scale diagram and calculation methods to find your answers.

Answer on p. 115

## Components of vectors

REVISED ☐

The effectiveness of the vector along a specified direction is called the **component** of the vector along this direction. Finding the components of a vector, usually along two perpendicular directions, is called the **resolution** of a vector.

The component of a vector along any direction is the magnitude of the vector multiplied by the cosine of the angle between the vector and the line.

The horizontal component of the vector **F** shown in Figure 4.3 (a) is $\mathbf{F}\cos A$, while Figure 4.3(b) shows the components of a vector in two perpendicular directions. These are known as the rectangular components of the vector.

Component in the $x$ direction: $\mathbf{F}_x = \mathbf{F}\cos A$

Component in the $y$ direction: $\mathbf{F}_y = \mathbf{F}\cos(90 - A) = \mathbf{F}\sin A$

### Typical mistake

Mixing up the angles when calculating components.

### Example

A railway truck is pulled along the rails by a rope that makes an angle of 35° with the track. If the force (**F**) in the rope is 1500 N calculate the components of the force:

(a) perpendicular to the rails

(b) parallel to the rails.

#### Answer

(a) component of **F** perpendicular to the rails = **F** sin 35 = 1500 × 0.574 = 860 N

(b) component of **F** parallel to the rails = **F** cos 35 = 1500 × 0.819 = 1229 N

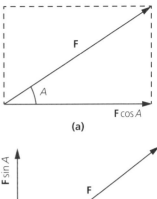

(a)

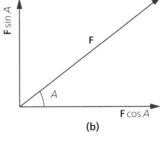

(b)

**Figure 4.3 Components of a vector**

## Now test yourself

TESTED

2 A tug pulls an ocean liner from its moorings. The cable from the bow of the liner to a tug makes an angle of 15° with the horizontal. If the force in the cable is 2000 N what are the horizontal and vertical components of this force?

Answer on p. 115

## The inclined plane

The components of the forces acting on a point object (P) on an inclined plane are shown in the Figure 4.4. The actual forces are the weight of the object represented by the black vector and the reaction of the plane, shown by the blue vector. The components of the weight are shown in red.

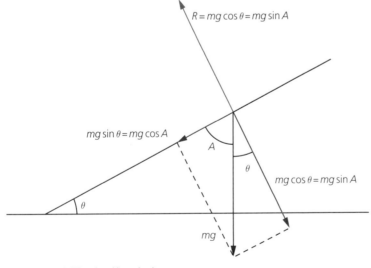

**Figure 4.4 The inclined plane**

## Equilibrium due to two or more forces

A body acted on by two or more forces is in equilibrium when it has no tendency to move. This means that:

**A body is in equilibrium when acted on by two or more coplanar forces if the resultant of these forces is zero and the two forces pass though one point.**

The resultant can be shown to be zero by calculating the components of each force in two perpendicular directions. Alternatively a scale diagram can be drawn. The resultant is zero when the forces form a closed triangle.

This can mean that an object in equilibrium can be at rest or moving with a constant velocity.

**Example**

Three forces of 100 N, 150 N and 200 N act on a body, as shown in Figure 4.5. Show that the resultant of these three forces is zero and that therefore the body is in equilibrium.

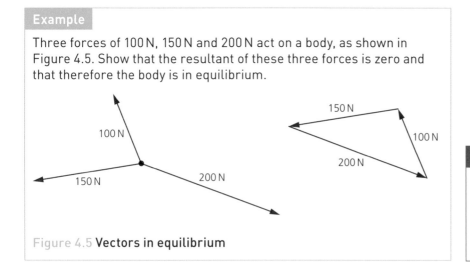

Figure 4.5 **Vectors in equilibrium**

**Exam tip**

For the body to be in equilibrium — no translation or rotation — the forces acting on it must pass through one point.

Note that, in Figure 4.5, the vectors are drawn 'nose to tail'.

# Moments

## Moment of a force about a point

REVISED

If a force acts on an object, and the line of action of the force does not pass through the centre of mass of the object then the force will exert a turning effect on the object and it will rotate. The larger the force and the further the line of action from the centre of mass the greater the turning effect of the force will be.

This turning effect is called the **moment of the force**.

**moment of a force** about a point = magnitude of force (*F*) × perpendicular distance (*d*) from the point to the line of action of the force:

moment = *Fd*

Moments are measured in Newton metres (Nm).

## Example

A light rod 80 cm long is pivoted about one end and supported by a vertical thread at the far end so that the rod makes an angle of 55° with the vertical. Calculate the moment of the force about the pivot if the force in the thread is 25 N.

Answer

See Figure 4.6.

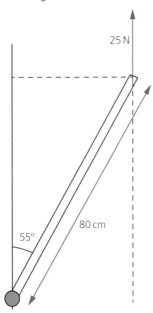

Figure 4.6 **Moments**

moment = force × perpendicular distance from the pivot to the line of action of the force

= 25 × 0.80 sin 55 = 16.4 Nm

**A body is in equilibrium when acted on by two or more coplanar forces if the resultant of these forces and their moments is zero.**

## Now test yourself

3 A door has a handle that is 0.8 m from the hinge. What is the moment of the following forces applied to the handle about the hinge?

(a) 12 N at right angles to the door

(b) 20 N at 70° to the door

(c) 100 N at 25° to the door

Answers on p. 115

Exam tip

Notice:
● the use of the perpendicular distance
● the conversion of cm to m to give the correct units (N m)

**Typical mistake**

Forgetting that the resultant moment must be zero when stating the condition for equilibrium.

TESTED

> If two equal and opposite forces, whose lines of action are not the same, act on a body, then they only produce a rotation of the body but no translation. This effect is called a **couple**.

A **couple** is composed of two forces that:
- are equal
- are anti-parallel (parallel but in opposite directions)
- do not pass through the same point.

Since a torque is caused by two forces rather than one the magnitude of the turning effect of a couple is called the **torque**.

> The **torque** of a couple is the product of one of the forces and the perpendicular distance between the lines of action of the forces.
>
> $$\text{torque} = \frac{F \times d}{2} \times 2 = Fd$$

### Example

Two forces, each of 30 N, act on a rod pivoted at its centre, as shown in Figure 4.7. The ends of the forces on the rod are 60 cm apart. Calculate the torque produced.

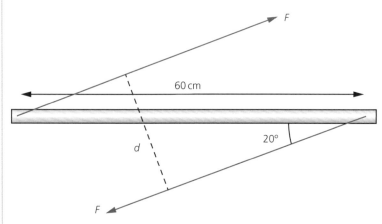

Figure 4.7 **A torque**

Answer

torque = force × perpendicular distance between the lines of action of the forces

torque = 30 × 0.60 sin 20 = 6.2 N m

### Now test yourself TESTED

4 One of the powered wheels of a car travelling at constant velocity has a torque of 140 N m applied to it by the axle that drives the car. If the wheel is 0.45 m in diameter, calculate the driving force provided by this wheel.

Answer on p. 115

# The principle of moments and equilibrium

**When an object is balanced (in equilibrium) the sum of the clockwise moments is equal and opposite to the sum of the anticlockwise moments (Figure 4.8).**

An example of the principle of moments is shown in Figure 4.8.

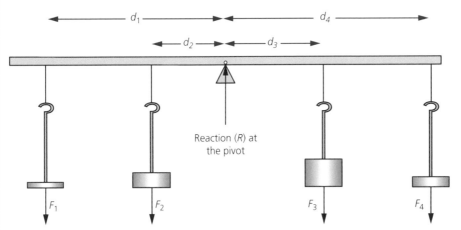

**Figure 4.8 Principle of moments**

$$F_1 d_1 + F_2 d_2 = F_3 d_3 + F_4 d_4$$

When an object is in equilibrium the sum of the vertical forces is zero.

$$F_1 + F_2 + F_3 + F_4 - R = 0$$

> **Exam tip**
>
> Notice the minus sign – $R$ acts in the opposite direction from $F_1$, $F_2$, $F_3$ and $F_4$.

> **Example**
>
> In Figure 4.9, let $L = 100\,cm$, $F_1 = 20\,N$, $F_3 = 10\,N$, $d_1 = 10\,cm$, $d_2 = 70\,cm$, $d_3 = 45\,cm$
>
>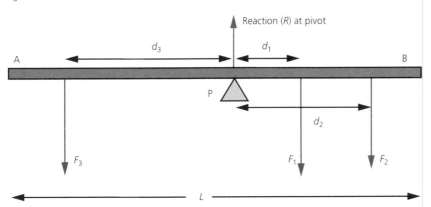
>
> Figure 4.9 **Example of the principle of moments**
>
> Find the value of $F_2$ such that the beam is in equilibrium.
>
> Answer
>
> Take moments about the pivot:
>
> clockwise moments = $(20 \times 0.1) + (F_2 \times 0.7) = 10 \times 0.45 =$ anticlockwise moments
>
> $2 + (F_2 \times 0.7) = 10 \times 0.45$
>
> $$F_2 = \frac{4.5 - 2}{0.7} = 3.6\,N$$

> **Exam tip**
>
> The moments can be taken about any point on an object. However, it may be more convenient to use one point than another if an unknown force passes through that point.

But:

$F_1 + F_2 + F_3 - R = 0$

and so:

$R = 20 + 3.6 + 10 = 33.6\,N$

## Now test yourself

5 A 3m long uniform plank of mass 6 kg is fixed to a wall by a pivot at P. It is supported by wire which makes an angle of 55° with the plank, and is fixed to it 0.6 m from the end furthest from the wall, as shown in Figure 4.10. ($g = 9.8\,m\,s^{-2}$)

Using the principle of moments calculate the tension ($T$) in the wire.

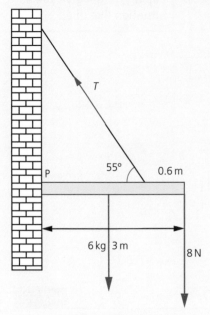

Figure 4.10 **Tension in a wire**

6 A lightweight beam 5.5 m long is fixed to a pivot. A load of 600 N is hung from one end and the beam is held in equilibrium by a vertical force $F$, as shown in Figure 4.11.

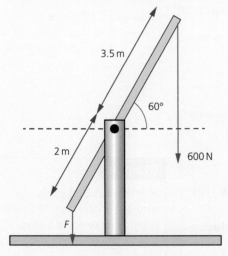

Figure 4.11 **A lightweight beam**

(a) Using the principle of moments calculate the value of $F$.
(b) How does $F$ change if the angle of the beam is changed?

Answers on p. 115

## Centre of gravity and centre of mass

The weight of an object may be taken as acting at one point known as the **centre of gravity**. You could think of that point as the position where all the mass of the object is concentrated.

**The resultant moment about the centre of gravity of any object must be zero.**

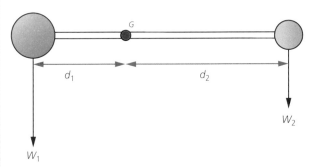

Figure 4.12 Centre of mass of an unequal dumbbell

**Exam tip**

If the gravitational field is uniform over the size of the object then the centre of mass and the centre of gravity of the object will coincide. However if this is not true then they will be in different places. Close to a black hole, where the gravitational field changes rapidly, might give you a situation like this.

The dumbbell arrangement in Figure 4.12 shows this clearly ($W_1 = m_1 g$; $W_2 = m_2 g$).

**anticlockwise moment = $W_1 \times d_1$; clockwise moment = $W_2 \times d_2$**

If all the mass was replaced by a mass of $M (= m_1 + m_2)$ at $G$ there would be no turning effect about $G$ and therefore the resultant moment must be zero.

# Motion along a straight line

## Displacement, speed, velocity and acceleration

**Speed** is defined as the rate of change of distance with time, while **velocity** is defined as the rate of change of displacement with time.

If an object is displaced by a small amount $\Delta s$ in a small time $\Delta t$ then its velocity $v$ is given by the equation:

$$\text{velocity, } v = \frac{\Delta s}{\Delta t}$$

**Displacement** is distance measured in a particular direction and **velocity** is speed measured in a particular direction. The units normally used for both speed and velocity are $\text{m s}^{-1}$.

Acceleration occurs when an object changes its velocity with time. The units normally used for acceleration are $\text{m s}^{-2}$:

$$\text{acceleration, } a = \text{rate of change of velocity} = \frac{\Delta v}{\Delta t} = \frac{\text{change in velocity}}{\text{time}}$$

**Exam tip**

Remember that distance and speed are scalars, while displacement and velocity are vectors.

# Using graphical methods to understand motion

## Displacement–time graphs

Figure 4.13 shows examples of displacement–time graphs. Uniform velocity is shown by straight lines and acceleration is shown by a curved line. The gradient at a point on a displacement–time curve is the instantaneous velocity at that point.

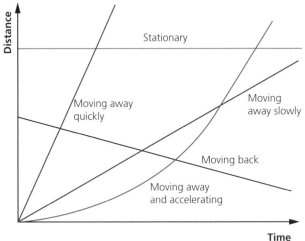

Figure 4.13 Displacement–time graphs

**Exam tip**

A displacement–time curve with a negative gradient shows an object moving in the opposite direction from one with a positive gradient.

## Velocity–time graphs

Figure 4.14 shows examples of velocity–time graphs. Uniform acceleration is shown by straight lines. Varying acceleration is shown by a curved line. The gradient at a point on a velocity–time curve is the instantaneous acceleration at that point.

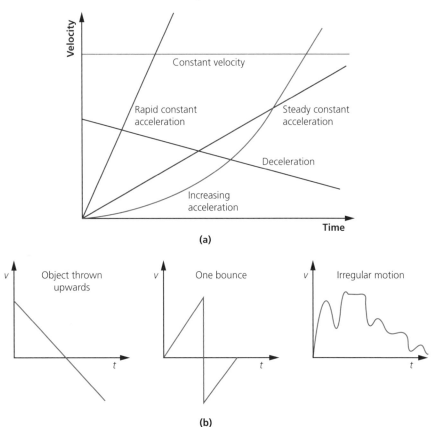

Figure 4.14 Velocity–time graphs

The area beneath a velocity–time graph is a measure of the displacement of the object (Figure 4.15).

**Exam tip**

This is true whatever the shape of the velocity–time curve.

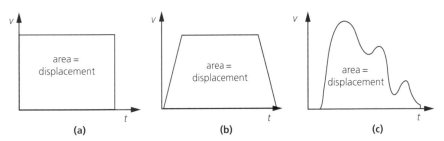

(a)   (b)   (c)

**Figure 4.15 Area under velocity–time graphs**

**Example**

Figure 4.16 shows the motion of a car.

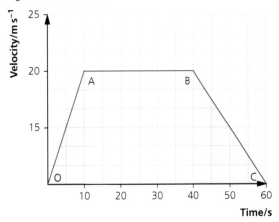

Figure 4.16 **Velocity–time graph example**

- O to A — the velocity increases steadily from $0\,m\,s^{-1}$ to $20\,m\,s^{-1}$ in 10 seconds.
- A to B — the velocity stays the same at $20\,m\,s^{-1}$ for the next 30 s.
- B to C — the velocity decreases to $0\,m\,s^{-1}$ in 20 s.

Using:

   distance = average velocity × time

Distance travelled OA = 10 × 10 = 100 m

Distance travelled AB = 20 × 30 = 600 m

Distance travelled BC = 10 × 20 = 200 m

Total distance travelled OC = 900 m

This is represented by the area under the line OABC.

**Typical mistake**

Forgetting that the equation $s = vt$ applies to uniform velocity only.

### Velocity–time graphs showing non-uniform acceleration

Problems of non-uniform acceleration can be solved by using graphical methods. One example is the 100 m sprint shown in Figure 4.17.

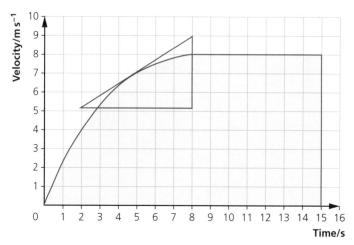

**Figure 4.17 Non-uniform acceleration**

The graph in Figure 4.17 shows the motion of a schoolgirl sprinter running the 100 m. It shows that her acceleration was not uniform but varied over the first 9 s of the race, after which it was zero.

The shaded area represents the distance she travelled in 15 s — in this case 100 m.

Her acceleration during the early part of the race can be found from the gradient of the curve at that point. For example, 5 s after the start her acceleration ($\Delta v/\Delta t$) was approximately $3.8/6 = 0.63 \, \mathrm{m \, s^{-2}}$.

## Now test yourself

7 The graph in Figure 4.18 shows a runner during part of a race. Using the graph find:

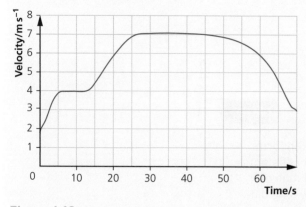

Figure 4.18

(a) the distance covered by the runner between 20 s and 60 s
(b) the velocity of the runner at $t = 15$ s
(c) the acceleration of the runner at $t = 55$ s.

Answers on p. 115

# Equations for uniform acceleration

If the acceleration of an object is uniform, the following equations apply to its motion:

$$\text{average velocity} = \frac{v+u}{2} \text{ or } s = \frac{u+v}{2}t$$

$$\text{acceleration, } a = \frac{v-u}{t} \text{ or } v = u + at$$

$$s = ut + \tfrac{1}{2}at^2$$

$$v^2 = u^2 + 2as$$

where $u$ is the initial velocity, $v$ the final velocity, $a$ the acceleration, $t$ the time taken and $s$ the displacement.

> **Exam tip**
>
> Remember that these equations only apply to accelerated motion when the acceleration is uniform.

## Example 1

A dragster starts from rests and accelerates at $25\,\text{m}\,\text{s}^{-2}$ for $4\,\text{s}$. Calculate:
(a) the final velocity
(b) the distance travelled.

Answer

(a) $v = u + at = 0 + (25 \times 4) = 100\,\text{m}\,\text{s}^{-1}$
(b) $s = \tfrac{1}{2}at^2 = 0.5 \times 25 \times 16 = 200\,\text{m}$

## Example 2

A ball travelling at $20\,\text{m}\,\text{s}^{-1}$ is hit by a bat and returned along its original path but in the opposite direction at $35\,\text{m}\,\text{s}^{-1}$. If the ball was in contact with the bat for $0.02\,\text{s}$ calculate:
(a) the acceleration of the ball during the hit
(b) the distance moved by the ball during the hit.

Answer

(a) $a = \dfrac{v-u}{t} = \dfrac{35-(-20)}{0.02} = \dfrac{55}{0.02} = 2750\,\text{m}\,\text{s}^{-2}$

(b) $v^2 = u^2 + 2as$

$s = \dfrac{35^2 - 20^2}{2 \times 2750} = 0.15\,\text{m}$

## Now test yourself

8  Starting from rest a car travels for 2 minutes with a uniform acceleration of $0.3\,\text{m}\,\text{s}^{-2}$ after which its speed is kept constant until the car is brought to rest with a uniform retardation of $0.6\,\text{m}\,\text{s}^{-2}$. If the total distance travelled is $4500\,\text{m}$ how long did the journey take?

9  An electron in a TV tube emitted from rest from a hot cathode reaches a velocity of $10^7\,\text{m}\,\text{s}^{-1}$ when it passes the anode. Find the acceleration of the electron if the cathode and anode are separated by $3\,\text{cm}$.

Answers on p. 115

# Acceleration due to gravity

The vertical acceleration in the Earth's gravitational field is due to the gravitational attraction of the Earth, and is called the acceleration due to gravity ($g$) or the **acceleration of free fall**. The value of $g$ close to the Earth's surface is about $9.81\,\text{ms}^{-2}$ (often simplified to $9.8\,\text{ms}^{-2}$ or even $10\,\text{ms}^{-2}$).

Since this acceleration is produced by the gravitational field of the Earth it may also be called the **gravitational intensity** (units $N\,\text{kg}^{-1}$).

If an object is dropped and falls through a height $h$ in $t$ seconds its acceleration is:

$$\text{gravitation acceleration } (g) = \frac{2h}{t^2}$$

If air resistance is neglected the acceleration in free fall is the same for all objects. This was suggested by Galileo Galilei in the seventeenth century.

> **Exam tip**
>
> You should always use the values of constants such as $g$ that are given in your exam question paper.

## Example

A stone falling from rest falls half its total path in the last second before it strikes the ground. From what height was it dropped?

**Answer**

For the complete path:

$h = \frac{1}{2}gt^2$

For the top half of its path:

$\dfrac{h}{2} = \frac{1}{2}g(t-1)^2$

So:

$h = \frac{1}{2}gt^2 = g(t^2 - 2t + 1)$

Therefore:

$t^2 = 2t^2 - 4t + 2$

and so:

$t^2 - 4t + 2 = 0$

This can be solved to give $t = 3.41\,\text{s}$ or $0.59\,\text{s}$. This last one is impossible since it fell half the distance in the last second.

Therefore:

$h = \frac{1}{2}gt^2 = \frac{1}{2} \times 9.8 \times 3.41^2 = 57.1\,\text{m}$

## Now test yourself

10  A stone is dropped from a cliff.
   (a) How far will it have fallen in 4 s?
   (b) What will its velocity be at that point?
   (c) What is the average velocity of the stone during the 4 s? (Use $g = 9.8\,\text{ms}^{-2}$ and ignore air resistance.)

Answer on p. 115

## Required practical 3

### Determination of *g*

The value of the gravitational acceleration (gravitational field intensity) at the Earth's surface may be found using a freefall method. A ball bearing is dropped from rest and the time (*t*) for it fall through a known height (*h*) is found. The measurements are repeated both for the original height and over a series of heights from 20 cm to 2 m.

The height fallen is measured with a ruler and the time of fall by a light gate or a mechanical gate mechanism.

$$\text{gravitational acceleration} = \frac{2h}{t^2}$$

# Projectile motion

## Objects projected vertically

If an object is projected upwards with an initial vertical velocity of *u*, such that its time of flight is 2*t* (in other words the time to return to the ground again) the time to reach the top of its trajectory is *t*. The velocity (*v*) at the top of the trajectory is zero.

maximum height, $h = \frac{1}{2}gt^2 = \frac{u^2}{2g}$

velocity, $v = u + gt$

**Exam tip**

Remember that the acceleration of the projectile is $9.8\,\text{m s}^{-2}$ towards the ground throughout the trajectory, even at the very top.

**Example**

A ball is thrown vertically upwards with an initial velocity of $30\,\text{m s}^{-1}$. Calculate:

(a) the maximum height reached
(b) the time taken for it to return to the ground.

$(g = 9.8\,\text{m s}^{-2})$

Answer

(a) Using $v^2 = u^2 + 2as$:

  $0 = 900 - 2 \times 9.8 \times s$

  $19.6s = 900$

  $s = 45.9\,\text{m}$

(Notice that at the maximum height the vertical velocity is zero and that the acceleration due to gravity is negative since it acts to retard the ball.)

(b) Using $v = u + at$:

  $30 = -30 + 9.8t$

  $t = 6.1\,\text{s}$

(Remember that the ball must return to the ground with the same speed with which it left it.)

# Objects projected horizontally

Figure 4.19 shows the motion of an object projected horizontally in a gravitational field.

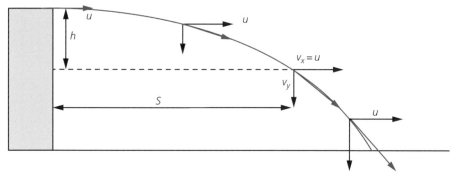

**Figure 4.19 Projectile: horizontal projection**

The object has:
- a motion in the horizontal direction — this is uniform velocity, since no forces act in this direction
- a motion in the vertical direction — this is uniformly accelerated motion due to the gravitational pull of the Earth, the vertical acceleration being the strength of the Earth's field ($g = 9.8\,\mathrm{m\,s^{-2}}$). Remember that this always acts vertically downwards.

> **Exam tip**
>
> The motion of a projectile should be thought of in two separate parts — one horizontal and the other vertical.

**The horizontal distance travelled ($s$) = horizontal velocity x time = $v_x t = ut$**

**The vertical distance travelled ($h$) = $u_y t + \frac{1}{2}(gt^2) = \frac{1}{2}(gt^2)$ since $u_y = 0$.**

**Velocity after a time $t$    $v = (v_x^2 + v_y^2)^{1/2}$**

**Direction of motion after time $t$    $\tan\theta = v_y/v_x$**

---

**Example**

A ball is thrown horizontally with an initial velocity of $6\,\mathrm{m\,s^{-1}}$ from an open window that is $4\,\mathrm{m}$ above the ground. Calculate:
(a) the time it takes to hit the ground
(b) the distance from the wall where it hits the ground
(c) the velocity (magnitude and direction) 0.5 seconds after it is thrown.

(Ignore air resistance in your calculations and take $g = 9.8\,\mathrm{m\,s^{-2}}$.)

*Answer*

(a) Using $h = \frac{1}{2}gt^2$:
   $4 = \frac{1}{2} \times 9.8 \times t^2$
   $t = 0.904\,\mathrm{s} = 0.90\,\mathrm{s}$
(b) $s = vt = 6 \times 0.904 = 5.42\,\mathrm{m}$
(c) vertical velocity after 0.5 s = $0 + gt = 9.8 \times 0.5 = 4.9\,\mathrm{m\,s^{-1}}$
   velocity after 0.5 s = $\sqrt{v_x^2 + v_y^2} = \sqrt{6^2 + 4.9^2} = 7.75\,\mathrm{m\,s^{-1}}$
   direction of motion: $\tan\theta = \dfrac{4.92}{6} = 0.82$ and so $\theta = 39.4°$

11  A crate is released from an aircraft that is flying horizontally, 1500 m above the ground, at a steady speed of 200 m s⁻¹.
  (a)  What is its horizontal velocity:
    (i)  2 s after it was released?        (ii)  5 s after it was released?
  (b)  What is its vertical velocity:
    (i)  2 s after it was released?        (ii)  5 s after it was released?
  (c)  What is its velocity (magnitude and direction) 5 s after it was released?
  (d)  How long will it take to reach the ground?
  (e)  How far horizontally from the place where it was released will it hit the ground?

($g = 9.8\,\text{m s}^{-2}$; air resistance can be ignored)

Answer on p. 115

## Objects projected at an angle                    REVISED ☐

Consider an object projected with velocity $u$ at an angle $A$ to the horizontal (Figure 4.20).

vertical component of velocity $= a\sin A$

horizontal component of velocity $= u\cos A$

Vertical motion: $h = ut\sin A - \tfrac{1}{2}gt^2$

Horizontal motion: $s = ut\cos A$

The maximum range for a given velocity of projection is when $\sin 2A = 1$, that is, when $2A = 90°$ or when $A = 45°$.

range $= \dfrac{u^2\sin 2A}{g}$

maximum height reached, $H = \dfrac{u^2\sin^2 A}{2g}$

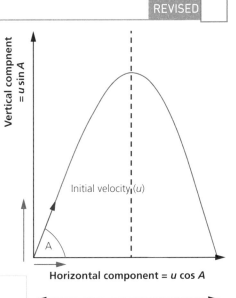

**Figure 4.20** Object projected at an angle

**Example**

A stone is projected at an angle of 60° to the horizontal with a velocity of 30 m s⁻¹. ($g = 9.8\,\text{m s}^{-2}$)

Calculate:
(a) the highest point reached
(b) the range
(c) the time taken for the flight
(d) the height of the stone at the instant that the path makes an angle of 30° with the horizontal.

Answer

(a) highest point $= \dfrac{30^2\sin^2 60°}{2g} = \dfrac{900 \times 0.75}{19.6} = 344\,\text{m}$

(b) range $= \dfrac{30^2\sin 120°}{9.8} = \dfrac{900 \times 0.866}{9.8} = 79.6\,\text{m}$

(c) time of flight $= \dfrac{2 \times 30\sin 60°}{9.8} = 5.3\,\text{s}$

(d) At the point when the path makes an angle of 30° to the horizontal:

$\tan 30° = \dfrac{\text{vertical component of velocity}}{\text{horizontal component of velocity}} = \dfrac{\text{vertical component}}{30\cos 60}$

The vertical component ($v$) is given by the formula:
$v^2 = 30^2 \sin^2 60° - (2 × 9.8 × h) = (900 × 0.75) - 19.6h$
where $h$ is the height reached at that point. Therefore:
$$\tan 30° = \frac{675 - 19.6h}{15}$$
$15 × 0.58 = 675 - 19.6h$
$8.66 = 675 - 19.6h$
$19.6h = 666.3$
$h = 34.0\,\text{m}$

## Now test yourself

TESTED

12  A projectile is fired from a siege engine at 35 m s⁻¹ at an angle of 60° to the horizontal:
   (a) What is its vertical velocity at the top of its flight?
   (b) What is its horizontal velocity at the top of its flight?
   (c) What is its acceleration at the top of its path?
   (d) What is its vertical velocity 5 s after it is fired?
   (e) What is its overall velocity 5 s after it is fired (magnitude and direction needed here).

Answer on p. 115

## Friction

REVISED

To move one body over another that is at rest requires a force. This is needed both to change the momentum of the first body and also to overcome the frictional force between the two surfaces. The force needed to overcome the frictional force when the bodies are at rest is called the **limiting friction** (often called static friction).

**The static frictional force between two surfaces depends on:**
● **the nature of the two surfaces**
● **the normal reaction between them**

When the object is moving the friction between the two surfaces is usually less than the static friction. This is almost independent of the relative velocities of the two surfaces.

## Lift and drag forces

REVISED

When a fluid is in motion the pressure within the fluid varies with the velocity of the fluid if the flow is streamlined.

**The pressure within a fast-moving fluid is lower than that in a similar fluid at rest or moving slowly.**

The shape of the cross-section of an aircraft wing is designed so that the velocity of the air above the wing is greater than that below it. A region of low pressure is created above the wing and so the aircraft experiences an upward force known as lift (Figure 4.21).

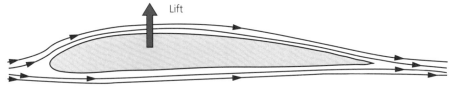

**Figure 4.21 Airflow over an aircraft wing**

## Terminal speed

REVISED

When any object falls through a fluid such as air it will experience a viscous drag.

As the object falls faster and faster the drag force increases. Eventually the drag force increases to a value where it is equal to the weight of the object and the body continues to fall at a steady speed. We call this the **terminal speed** of the object (Figure 4.22).

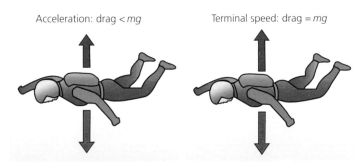

Acceleration: drag < *mg*      Terminal speed: drag = *mg*

**Figure 4.22 Terminal speed**

At the terminal speed:

**viscous drag (air resistance) = weight of the object = *mg***

Figure 4.23 shows how the velocity of an object will increase with time as it falls through a viscous fluid. The acceleration starts with a value of *g* but falls to zero when the terminal speed is reached.

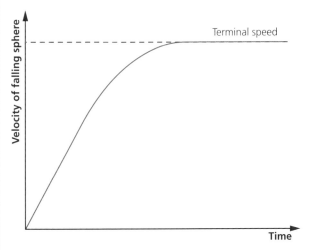

**Figure 4.23 Terminal speed graph**

# Newton's laws of motion

## Newton's first law of motion

REVISED

Newton's first law of motion states that:

> **A body remains at rest or in a state of uniform motion unless acted on by a resultant force.**

## At rest

Someone sitting on a stool may be at rest but they are acted on by two forces — their weight and the reaction of the stool. It is because these two forces are balanced and there is no resultant force that they stay still — i.e. at rest.

## Uniform motion

This means no change of velocity; since velocity is a vector, this means at a steady speed in a straight line. As a skydiver falls out of a plane their speed increases — their weight is bigger than the drag — so there is a net force and Newton's first law does not apply. However, as the drag increases the two forces on them become equal and the skydiver falls with a constant velocity — a state of uniform motion.

## Newton's second law of motion

REVISED

You need a force to change the motion of a body. The bigger the net force the greater the acceleration. (Remember that force is a vector and the direction of the forces acting on a body need to be considered.)

**Newton's second law of motion suggests that:**
- **acceleration is directly proportional to the accelerating force**
- **acceleration is inversely proportional to the mass of the body being accelerated**

$$\text{force} = \text{mass} \times \text{acceleration}$$

$$F = ma$$

The units for force are Newtons (N), those for mass are kg and those for acceleration $ms^{-2}$.

This law also gives us a good definition of the Newton as a unit of force.

**One newton is the force that will give a mass of 1 kilogram an acceleration of $1\,ms^{-2}$.**

### Example

A 250 kg box is pulled along a smooth road (no frictional drag) using a force of 2000 N. What is the acceleration of the block?

Answer

Using $F = ma$:

$$a = \frac{F}{m} = \frac{2000}{250} = 8\,ms^{-2}$$

### Exam tip

Note that it is mass that is used in the equation, mass is measured in kg. Do not convert mass to a weight.

### Now test yourself

TESTED

13 At the start of a 100 m race the rear foot of a sprinter can exert a force of some 1150 N on the starting blocks and the front foot an additional 800 N. If the sprinter is a man of mass 83 kg what is his initial acceleration?
14 If a rocket has a mass of 50 000 kg and its motors exert a thrust of 550 000 N what is the initial vertical acceleration off the rocket? ($g = 9.8\,ms^{-2}$)

Answers on p. 115

# Newton's third law of motion

This states that:

> **If a force acts on one body, an equal and opposite force acts on another body.**
>
> *or*
>
> **Action and reaction are equal and opposite.**

This law can be checked by fixing two spring-loaded trucks together on a linear air track. When the spring is released they *both move off*, showing that there is a force on *both*, with the acceleration of each truck depending on its mass.

The two forces mentioned in Newton's third law are known as a 'Newton pair' (Figure 4.24).

**Figure 4.24 A Newton pair**

A Newton pair of forces has the following properties:
- The two forces act on two different bodies.
- Both forces are always of the same type (i.e. both gravitational, both electrostatic, etc.).
- The forces are equal in magnitude.
- The forces act in opposite directions.

A book on a table can be used to explain the idea of a Newton pair. In this example there are *two* Newton pairs:
- Gravitational forces — the pull of the Earth on the book and the pull of the book on the Earth.
- Contact forces — the push of the book on the table and the push of the table on the book.

> **Exam tip**
>
> Notice that in each case if one of the forces of the pair is removed it makes the other one vanish.

## Now test yourself

TESTED

15 A car of mass 1000 kg pulls a caravan of mass 800 kg. The driving wheels of the car exert a force of 8000 N on the road. The total resistance to motion is 3000 N.
  (a) What is the net accelerating force?
  (b) What is the acceleration?
  (c) What is the force of the car on the caravan?

Answer on p. 115

# Momentum

## Impulse

REVISED

> When a force acts on a body the velocity of the body may change. The product of the force and the time for which it acts is called the **impulse**.
>
> impulse = force × time        (units N s)

If application of an **impulse** is represented by a force–time graph, the impulse is the area beneath the line on the graph (Figures 4.25 and 4.26).

## Momentum and momentum change

REVISED

> The change in the velocity of a body due to the action of an impulse depends not only on the size of the impulse but also the mass of the body. The product of the mass of the body and its velocity is called the **momentum** of the body.
>
> **momentum = mass × velocity      (units kg m s⁻¹)**
>
> Therefore, an impulse produces a change of momentum.

If the velocity of a body of mass $m$ is changed from $u$ to $v$ by a force $F$ acting for a time $t$:

impulse = $Ft$ = momentum change $(\Delta mv)$ = $mv - mu$   (units kg m s⁻¹ or N s)

Force may therefore be written as:

$$\text{force = rate of change of momentum } F = \frac{\Delta mv}{\Delta t}$$

> **Exam tip**
>
> Remember that momentum, and therefore momentum change, is a vector.

> **Example**
>
> Figure 4.25 shows an impulse of 8 N being applied to a body for 20 s.
>
>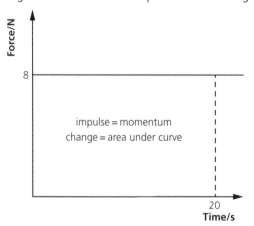
>
> Figure 4.25 **Force–time graph**
>
> Both the impulse and the momentum change are the area under the line. Therefore:
>
> impulse = 8 × 20 = 160 N s

## Now test yourself

16 The graph in Figure 4.26 shows a varying force being applied to a body. If the body has a mass of 2.5 kg, calculate the impulse and hence the change in the velocity of the body during the first 10 s of the motion shown.

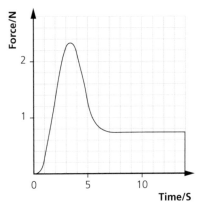

Figure 4.26 **Force–time graph, with variable force**

Answer on p.115

## Conservation of momentum

REVISED ☐

Momentum is conserved in a collision or explosion in an isolated system where no external forces act. In other words the momentum before the collision or explosion is the same as that after it. This is true for *all* collisions and explosions.

**momentum before collision = momentum after collision**

In a collision the same law of conservation of momentum applies. If a mass $m_1$ moving at a velocity $u_1$ collides with a mass $m_2$ moving at a velocity $u_2$ such that after the collision $m_1$ moves at $v_1$ and $m_2$ moves at $v_2$:

$$m_1u_1 + m_2u_2 = m_1v_1 + m_2v_2$$

The law of conservation of momentum applies whether the collisions are elastic or not (Figure 4.27).

**Figure 4.27 Elastic collision**

The special case of two equal masses making a completely elastic collision is shown in Figure 4.28. In this collision the velocities of A and B are swapped over.

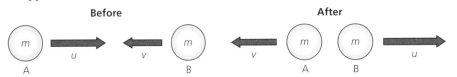

**Figure 4.28 Elastic collision — equal masses**

In a perfectly inelastic collision all the kinetic energy of the colliding bodies is lost — this may be converted into heat or used to deform the bodies. Imagine two balls colliding head on, sticking together and then moving off after the collision.

**Figure 4.29 Perfectly inelastic collision**

## Explosions

REVISED

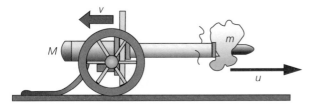

**Figure 4.30 Cannon firing a shell**

Energy and momentum are also conserved in explosions, although the type of energy may be changed. For example when a cannon fires a shell the total momentum of the shell ($mu$) (plus that of any exhaust gases etc.) and the cannon ($Mv$) is the same after firing as it was before firing — that is, zero.

> **Exam tip**
>
> In an explosion where two fragments are produced the heavier fragment will have the smaller velocity.

**Momentum before explosion = momentum after explosion**

**Therefore: $0 = mu + Mv$**

$Mv = -mu$

> **Example**
>
> If a mass of 3.5 kg moving left to right at 5 m s⁻¹ collides with a mass of 4.0 kg moving right to left at 3.0 m s⁻¹ and they stick together, find the final velocity of the combined masses.
>
> **Answer**
>
> momentum before impact = (3.5 × 5.0) + (−4.0 × 3.0) = 5.5 N s
>
> But this must equal the momentum after the collision, i.e. total mass × final velocity.
>
> Notice that one of the velocities is negative, showing that the ball was moving right to left.
>
> mass afterwards = 7.5 kg
>
> Therefore:
>
> velocity afterwards = $\dfrac{5.5}{7.5}$ = 0.73 m s⁻¹
>
> This is positive, showing that after collision the combined two balls move from left to right.

17 A child throws a 200 g snowball with a speed of 8 m s⁻¹ so that it hits the 1.5 kg head of a snowman. The snowball sticks to the snowman's head and knocks it off. What is the initial velocity of the ball and head just after collision?

Answer on p. 115

# Work, energy and power

## Work                                                                                             REVISED

When a force moves an object **work** is done on the object and energy is converted from one form to another. The units for work are joule (J).

> **work done = force × displacement**
>
> **= force × displacement in the direction of the force**
>
> **work done = $F(s \cos \theta)$**

> **Exam tip**
>
> Force and displacement are both vectors but work is a scalar.

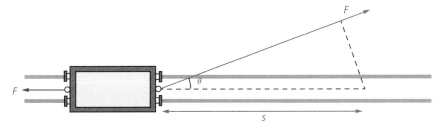

**Figure 4.31 Work done by a force**

Figure 4.31 shows a truck being pulled at a constant velocity a distance $s$ along a pair of rails by a force $F$. The force is applied at an angle $\theta$ to the rails. The truck has a displacement $s$ along the rails and the truck moves a distance $s \cos \theta$ in the direction of the force $F$.

If there were no friction between the rails and the truck, the force needed to keep the truck moving would be zero. However if there is a force of friction $F'$ between the rails and the truck, once the truck is moving it will require a force $F \cos \theta$ (= $F'$) acting left to right to keep the truck moving at a constant velocity.

> **Exam tip**
>
> In the extreme case of the force acting at right angles to the rails the truck would not move along the rails and the work done on the truck would be zero. Clearly the most effective direction in which to apply the force to the truck if we want it to move along the rails is parallel to the rails.

> **Example 1**
>
> Calculate the minimum work done to pull a truck 8 m along a pair of rails at constant velocity if the frictional force opposing the motion is 100 N.
>
> **Answer**
>
> In this case the minimum work done would be when the force is parallel to the rails.
>
> work done = force × displacement = 100 × 8 = 800 J

**Example 2**

The force is now applied at an angle of 30° to the rails. If the frictional force remains the same, calculate:

(a) the force required to keep the truck moving at the same constant velocity along the rails

(b) the work done in moving the truck 8 m along the rails.

**Answer**

(a) force $(F)\cos\theta$ = frictional force = 100 N

(b) Therefore:

$$F = \frac{100}{\cos 30} = 115.5\,N$$

work done = 115.5 × 8 = 923.8 J

The work done on an object is the area under the line in a force–displacement graph. This applies if the force is constant (Figure 4.32(a)) or varying (Figure 4.32(b)).

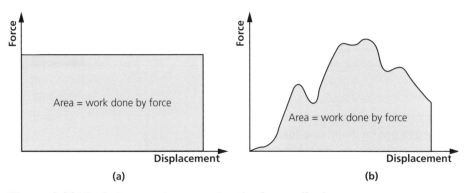

**(a)**                    **(b)**

**Figure 4.32** Work done and area under the force–displacement curve

**work done against the force of gravity = $mg\Delta h$**

where $\Delta h$ is the change in height of the object above some original position measured upwards from that position.

## Now test yourself

TESTED ☐

18  A man pulls a boat along a canal at a constant speed using a rope that makes an angle of 30° with the direction that the boat moves along the canal. If the force in the rope is 500 N calculate:

(a) the component of force along the canal

(b) the component of the force at right angles to the canal

(c) the work done by the man to move the boat 40 m along the canal.

Answer on p. 115

## Power

REVISED

The rate at which work is done, or the rate at which energy is converted from one form to another is the **power**, and is defined as:

$$\text{power, } P = \frac{\text{work done}}{\text{time taken}} = \frac{\Delta W}{\Delta t}$$

The units of power are watts (W), where 1 watt is 1 joule per second.

**Exam tip**

Power can also be expressed as:

power = force ($F$) × velocity ($v$)

### Now test yourself

TESTED

19 A car travelling at $30\,\text{m s}^{-1}$ along a level road is brought to rest in a distance of $35\,\text{m}$ by its brakes. If the total frictional drag at $30\,\text{m s}^{-1}$ is $5000\,\text{N}$ and the force exerted by the brakes during braking is $7000\,\text{N}$ calculate:
   (a) the power of the car when travelling at $30\,\text{m s}^{-1}$
   (b) the work done by the brakes to bring it to rest.

Answer on p. 115

## Energy

REVISED

### Efficiency

Machines are devices for converting (transforming) one form of 'useful' energy to another form of 'useful' energy. How effective the machine is at making this transformation is called the **efficiency** of the machine.

$$\text{efficiency} = \frac{\text{useful energy transferred in a given time}}{\text{energy supplied in that time}} \times 100\%$$

A petrol engine is about 30% efficient, a diesel engine 40% efficient and our bodies are a mere 25% efficient — only one quarter of the energy produced goes to moving the muscles.

# Conservation of energy

### Principle of energy conservation

REVISED

It is important to talk about the transformation or conversion of energy from one form to another and not its use. This is because although we may use up energy in one form it always reappears as another.

The principle of **conservation of energy** is that energy is never created or destroyed but only transformed from one form of energy to another.

# Sources of energy

REVISED

These include:

- fossil fuels — coal, oil, gas
- wind
- waves
- tides
- peat
- hydroelectric
- pumped storage
- nuclear fission
- nuclear fusion
- solar
- osmotic pressure
- geothermal
- biomass

# Different forms of energy

REVISED

Energy can 'exist' in the following forms:

- mechanical (kinetic, gravitational potential)
- tensile
- nuclear
- heat (radiant, kinetic)
- magnetic
- sound (kinetic)
- electrical
- chemical
- mass

## Gravitational potential energy

The energy associated with the position of a body of mass $m$ in a gravitational field is the **gravitational potential energy** of the body compared with some reference point where $h = 0$ — usually the surface of the Earth.

If the distance moved parallel to the gravitational field is $\Delta h$ then the change in potential energy is:

**gravitational potential energy change = $mg\Delta h$**

> **Exam tip**
>
> Remember that in gravitational potential energy changes it is the vertical height moved in the field that is important.

### Example 1

A crane lifts a load of 300 kg through a distance of 2.5 m onto a truck. Calculate the gain in gravitational potential energy. (gravitational field intensity = 9.8 N kg$^{-1}$).

**Answer**

gravitational potential energy gained = $mg\Delta h$ = 300 × 9.8 × 2.5 = 7350 J

### Example 2

A mass of 25 kg is moved a distance of 35 m at an angle of 20° to a gravitational field of intensity 9.8 N kg$^{-1}$. Calculate the change in gravitational energy.

**Answer**

change in gravitational potential energy = 25 × 9.8 × 35 cos 20 = 8058 J

## Now test yourself

TESTED ☐

20 An 85 kg athlete trains by running up a flight of 30 steps. If each step is 15 cm high and 20 cm wide calculate the change in his gravitational potential energy. (gravitational field intensity = 9.8 N kg$^{-1}$)

Answer on p. 115

## Kinetic energy

> The energy possessed by a body by virtue of its motion is called the **kinetic energy** of the body.

The **kinetic energy** of an object depends on two things:
● the mass of the object ($m$)
● its speed ($v$)

The formula for kinetic energy of an object of mass $m$ travelling at velocity $v$ is:

$$\text{kinetic energy} = \tfrac{1}{2}mv^2$$

### Kinetic energy changes

It is important to understand the correct way to calculate changes in the kinetic energy of an object. For example, suppose we want to find the increase in the kinetic energy of an 8 kg ball when its velocity is increased from 3 m s$^{-1}$ to 4 m s$^{-1}$. The correct way is as follows:

kinetic energy increase ($\Delta$ke) = $\tfrac{1}{2}$ × 8 × (4$^2$ – 3$^2$) = 4 × (16 – 9) = 4 × 7 = 28 J

and *not*

kinetic energy increase = $\tfrac{1}{2}$ × 8 × (4 – 3)$^2$ = 4 J

**Exam tip**

Check that you understand the correct way of calculating kinetic energy changes.

### Example 1

A lorry of mass 6000 kg travels along a level road at 30 m s$^{-1}$. The brakes are then applied and the lorry stops in 70 m. Calculate:
(a) the kinetic energy of the lorry before braking
(b) the braking force.

Answer

(a) kinetic energy = $\tfrac{1}{2}mv^2$ = $\tfrac{1}{2}$ × 6000 × 30$^2$ = 2 700 000 J = 2.7 MJ

(b) braking force = $\dfrac{\text{energy change}}{\text{braking distance}}$ = $\dfrac{2.7 \times 10^6}{70}$ = 38.6 kN

### Example 2

A lorry of mass 2000 kg moving at $10\,\mathrm{m\,s^{-1}}$ on a horizontal surface is brought to rest in a distance of 12.5 m by the brakes being applied.
(a) Calculate the average retarding force ($F$).
(b) What power must the engine produce if the lorry is to travel up a hill of 1 in 10 at a constant speed of $10\,\mathrm{m\,s^{-1}}$ the frictional resistance being 200 N?

#### Answer

(a) kinetic energy of lorry = $\frac{1}{2} \times 2000 \times 100 = 10^5\,\mathrm{J} = F \times 12.5$

Therefore $F = 8000\,\mathrm{N}$

(b) On the hill, height risen per second = 1 m and distance travelled along the slope = 10 m.

potential energy gained by lorry per second (taking $g = 9.8\,\mathrm{N\,kg^{-1}}$) = $2000 \times 9.8 \times 1 = 19\,600\,\mathrm{J}$

work done against friction per second = $200 \times 10 = 2000\,\mathrm{J}$

total energy required per second = $21\,600\,\mathrm{W} = 21.6\,\mathrm{kW}$

**Exam tip**

Remember that both gravitational energy and kinetic energy are scalars.

## Now test yourself

TESTED ☐

21 What is the maximum speed at which an earth-mover of mass 250000 kg can descend a slope of 1 in 10 if the brakes can dissipate energy at a maximum rate of 2000 kW? ($g = 9.8\,\mathrm{N\,kg^{-1}}$)

22 A lift has a mass of 400 kg. A man of mass 70 kg stands on a weighing machine fixed to the floor of the lift. Four seconds after starting from rest the lift has reached its maximum speed and has risen 5 m.
 (a) What will be the reading on the weighing machine during the period of acceleration?
 (b) How may it be decided whether the acceleration was uniform?
 (c) How much energy will be used by the lift motor in:
  (i) the first four seconds
  (ii) the next four seconds?

Answers on p. 115

# Bulk properties of solids

## Density

REVISED ☐

The mass of individual atoms and how closely they are packed together can be 'felt' on an everyday level — it is called the **density** of the material.

$$\text{density, } \rho = \frac{\text{mass}}{\text{volume}} = \frac{m}{V}$$

### Example

A statue has a volume of $5 \times 10^{-4}\,\text{m}^3$ and a mass of $4.75\,\text{kg}$. It has been made of copper (density $8930\,\text{kg}\,\text{m}^{-3}$) with a layer of silver (density $10500\,\text{kg}\,\text{m}^{-3}$) on top. What are the masses of copper and silver in the statue?

#### Answer

mass = volume × density

$4.75 = \rho_{Cu}V_{Cu} + \rho_{Ag}V_{Ag} = 8930\,V_{Cu} + 10500\,V_{Ag}$

But $V_{Cu} + V_{Ag} = 5 \times 10^{-4}$ and therefore $4.75 = 8930\,V_{Cu} + 10500(5 \times 10^{-4} - V_{Cu})$.

Therefore:

$V_{Cu} = \dfrac{0.5}{1570} = 3.18 \times 10^{-4}\,\text{m}^3$

So:

$V_{Ag} = 1.82 \times 10^{-4}\,\text{m}^3$

mass of copper = $8930 \times 3.18 \times 10^{-4} = 2.84\,\text{kg}$

mass of silver = $1.91\,\text{kg}$

> **Exam tip**
>
> Remember to use the correct SI units when calculating and expressing density.

### Now test yourself

TESTED

23 $3\,\text{mg}$ of gas are injected into the vacuum chamber of a fusion reactor. The volume of the chamber containing the gas is $3.75\,\text{m}^3$. What is the density of the gas under these conditions?

Answer on p. 115

## Hooke's law and the elastic limit

REVISED

The simplest form of variation of the extension of a metal wire when a stretching force is applied to it is known as **Hooke's law**. It relates the applied force ($F$), or load, to the increase in length, or extension ($\Delta L$), of the object.

> **Hooke's law** states that if the elastic limit is not exceeded the extension is directly proportional to the applied force — doubling the force will double the extension.
>
> **force = constant × extension**
>
> $F = k\Delta L$
>
> The constant $k$ is known as the **elastic constant** for the material and is defined as $F/\Delta L$. The units for $k$ are $\text{N}\,\text{m}^{-1}$.

If a graph of force is plotted against extension a straight line will be obtained up to a certain point called the **elastic limit** (shown as P on the graph in Figure 4.33). Up to the elastic limit the wire behaves elastically — that is, it will return to its original length if the load is removed. Beyond the elastic limit the wire will remain permanently stretched.

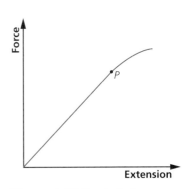

Figure 4.33 Hooke's law

## Example

An elastic cord has an unstretched length of 35 cm. One end is fixed to a support, and when a force of 2 N is applied to the lower end the length of the cord is 65 cm.

Calculate the elastic constant of the cord.

Answer

elastic constant, $k = \dfrac{\text{force}}{\text{extension}} = \dfrac{2}{0.3} = 6.7\,\text{N}\,\text{m}^{-1}$

## Now test yourself

24 A load of 50 N is hung on a 2.50 m length of copper wire. The elastic constant for the wire is 9400 N m$^{-1}$. Calculate the new length of the wire.

Answer on p. 115

# Tensile stress and tensile strain

## Tensile stress

Every elastic **stress** produces an elastic **strain**.

Tensile **stress** is a measure of the cause of the deformation produced by a force:

$$\text{tensile stress, } \sigma = \frac{\text{force}}{\text{area normal to the force}}$$

The units for tensile stress are N m$^{-2}$ or Pa.

## Tensile strain

**Strain** is a measure of the deformation produced by the stress:

$$\text{tensile strain, } \varepsilon = \frac{\text{extension}}{\text{original length}}$$

Strain has no units as it is simply a ratio of two quantities with the same units.

# Breaking stress

The maximum stress that a material can stand before it breaks is called the breaking stress. There are two types of breaking stress:
- compressive breaking stress — the maximum squashing stress before fracture
- tensile breaking stress — the maximum stretching stress before fracture

**Example**

The compressive breaking stress (F) of a material can be used to work out the maximum height of a rock column that is possible on the surface of the Earth (Figure 4.34).

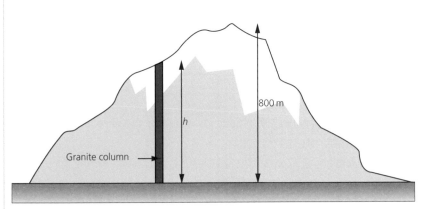

Figure 4.34 **Maximum height of a granite column**

maximum pressure at the base = $F = \rho g h$, where $\rho$ is the density of the rock.

For granite:

$F = 145 \times 10^6$ and $\rho = 2500 \, \text{kg m}^{-3}$

So:

$$h = \frac{145 \times 10^6}{2500 \times 9.81} = 5900 \, \text{m}$$

This is smaller than the height of many mountains but in a mountain the 'column' of rock would be supported from the sides by the rest of the mountain.

## Now test yourself

TESTED

25 A lift and its passengers have a combined a weight of 20 000 N. The lift is suspended from four steel cables of equal diameter. Calculate the minimum diameter of each cable, allowing for a 50% safety margin. (breaking stress for steel = 500 MPa)

Answer on p. 115

## Elastic strain energy

REVISED

When a person jumps up and down on a trampoline it is clear that the bed of the trampoline stores energy when it is in a state of tension. This energy is converted to kinetic and gravitational potential energy of the jumper when the tension is removed.

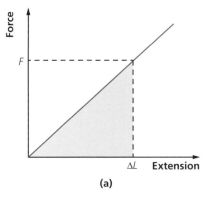 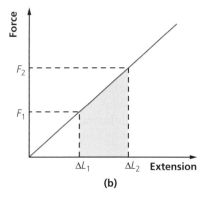

(a)  (b)

**Figure 4.35 Elastic strain energy**

Consider a wire of unstretched length $L$ and let a force $F$ produce an extension $\Delta L$. Assume that the elastic limit of the wire has not been exceeded and that no energy is converted to other forms such as heat (Figure 4.35(a)).

The work done by a force is $Fs$ but in this case the force varies from 0 at the start to $F$ at the end when the wire is stretched by an amount $\Delta L$. Therefore:

**elastic energy stored in the wire = ½$F\Delta L$**

But the work done by the force $F$ is equal to the energy gained by the wire. Therefore:

**work done on the wire during stretching = average force × extension**
**= ½$F\Delta L$**

This energy is the shaded area of the graph.

If the extension is increased from $\Delta L_1$ to $\Delta L_2$ (Figure 4.35(b)) then the extra energy stored is given by:

**additional elastic energy stored in the wire = ½$F(\Delta L_2 - \Delta L_1)$**

### Example

Calculate the energy stored in a stretched copper wire if its extension is increased by 1.5 mm when the force applied to it is increased by 50 N.

**Answer**

additional energy stored = ½$F(\Delta L_2 - \Delta L_1)$ = ½ × 50 × 1.5 × 10$^{-3}$ = 0.0375 J

### Now test yourself

26 Calculate the increase in the elastic energy stored in the string of a cello if an increase in tension from 0 to 70 N produces an extension of 1 mm.

Answer on p. 116

A **ductile** material is one such as copper, which may be drawn out into a wire without fracture. If a ductile material is stretched beyond its elastic limit it will show **plastic** behaviour. This means that when the load is removed some, or all, the deformation will be permanent and the material will not return to its original length before stretching.

Materials such as glass that can be extended but do not show plastic deformation and will easily fracture are known as **brittle** materials.

## Stress–strain curves

If a ductile material such as copper is stretched it will follow the curve shown by Figure 4.36(a). From O to P Hooke's law is obeyed. The point E is the elastic limit — if the load is removed before E is reached the material will return to its original length. Between E and Y the material becomes plastic — not all the extension is recoverable if the load is removed. B is the breaking stress at which the material fractures.

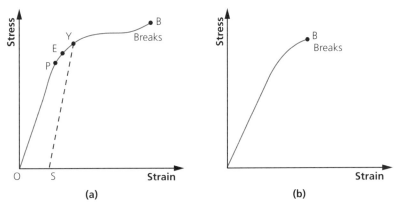

Figure 4.36 Ductile and brittle materials

Figure 4.36(b) shows the stress–strain curve for a brittle material. There is no plastic deformation.

# The Young modulus

The **Young modulus** determines the relation between tensile stress and tensile strain (Figure 4.37).

Figure 4.37 The Young modulus

> The **Young modulus** is the ratio of tensile stress to tensile strain:
>
> $$\text{tensile stress} = \frac{\text{force}}{\text{cross sectional area}} = \frac{F}{A}$$
>
> $$\text{tensile strain} = \frac{\text{extension}}{\text{original length}} = \frac{\Delta L}{L}$$
>
> $$\text{Young modulus} = \frac{\text{tensile stress}}{\text{tensile strain}} = \frac{\sigma}{\varepsilon} = \frac{F/A}{\Delta L/L} = \frac{FL}{A\Delta L}$$

### Example

A steel wire 10 m long and with a cross-sectional area of 0.01 cm² is hung from a support and a load of 150 N is applied to its lower end. Calculate the new length of the wire. (Young modulus for steel = 210 GPa)

**Answer**

$$\text{extension, } \Delta L = \frac{150 \times 10}{2.1 \times 10^{11} \times 1 \times 10^{-6}} = 7.14\,\text{mm}$$

Therefore, the new length = 10.00714 m

## Now test yourself

TESTED ☐

27 The rubber cord of a catapult has a cross-sectional area of 1.0 mm² and a total unstretched length of 10.0 cm. It is stretched to 15 cm and then released to project a missile of mass 5.0 g vertically. Calculate:
   (a) the energy stored in the rubber
   (b) the velocity of projection
   (c) the maximum height that the missile could reach.
   Take the Young modulus for rubber to be $5.0 \times 10^8$ Pa and $g = 9.8\,\text{N kg}^{-1}$.

28 It has been calculated that during running the force on the hip joint is about five times the body weight. Estimate the compression of the femur during each running stride for a sprinter of mass 70 kg. (Assume that the femur is 0.40 m long and has a mean diameter of 2.0 cm; $g = 9.8\,\text{N kg}^{-1}$; Young modulus for bone = $18 \times 10^9$ Pa.)

29 A gymnast of mass 70 kg hangs by one arm from a high bar. If the gymnast's whole weight is assumed to be taken by the humerus bone (in the upper arm) calculate the stress in the humerus if it has a radius of 1.5 cm. ($g = 9.8\,\text{N kg}^{-1}$)

Answers on p. 116

## Required practical 4

### Measurement of the Young modulus

The Young modulus can be measured for a material in the form of a wire using the apparatus shown in Figure 4.38.

Two identical wires are hung from a beam; one wire is used as a reference standard and has a scale is fixed to one wire and a mass hung on the end to remove kinks in it. The other wire has a small load placed on it to straighten it and a vernier scale that links with the scale on the reference wire.

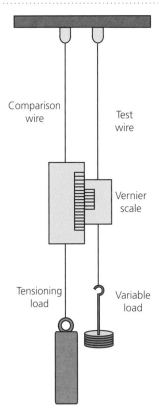

**Figure 4.38** Measurement of the Young modulus

The original length (*L*) of the test wire is measured and its diameter is found for various points along its length.

Loads are then placed gently on the wire and the extension of the wire found for each one. They should not be dropped, as this would subject the wire to a sudden shock. After each reading the load should be removed to check that the wire returns to its original length, showing that its elastic limit has not been exceeded.

A graph is plotted of stress against strain and from this the value of the Young modulus can be found (this is the gradient of the line, i.e. $F/A$ divided by $\Delta L/L$).

## Exam practice

Take $g$ = 9.8 N kg$^{-1}$ where needed.

1  An oarsman rows a boat across a river that is flowing from left to right at 10 m s$^{-1}$. If the speed of the boat at right angles to the bank is 6 m s$^{-1}$ find the final velocity of the boat as it moves across the river.  [4]
   You should use both the scale diagram and calculation methods to find your answers.

2  A child pulls a 120 kg sledge along a rough level road using a rope that is inclined at 35° to the horizontal. If the force in the rope is 300 N and the frictional force between the sledge and the road is 20 N what is the acceleration of the sledge?  [3]

3  A stone is projected upwards at 25 m s$^{-1}$ at an angle of 30° to the horizontal (air resistance should be ignored for parts (a)–(d)):
   (a)  What is its vertical velocity at the top of its flight?  [1]
   (b)  What is its horizontal velocity at the top of its flight?  [2]
   (c)  What is its horizontal velocity 5 s after it is fired?  [2]
   (d)  What is the maximum height it reaches?  [3]
   (e)  Sketch the trajectory of the projectile for the following two cases:
        (i)   when air resistance is ignored  [2]
        (ii)  when air resistance is taken into account  [3]

4 A rigid body acted on by a set of forces is in equilibrium if:
   A   the resultant force is zero
   B   the forces all act in the same direction and the resultant couple is zero
   C   the resultant force and the resultant couple are both zero
   D   the resultant couple is zero [1]

5 A uniform ladder 3 m long and weighing 200 N leans against a wall so that it makes an angle of 55° with the ground. $(g = 9.8 \, \text{N kg}^{-1})$
   (a) What is the normal reaction between the ladder and the wall? [3]
   (b) What is the size and direction of the reaction at the ground? [3]
   (c) A painter of mass 70 kg climbs the ladder. Calculate the new values for parts (a) and (b) when they are 1.0 m up the ladder (measured along the ladder itself). [4]

6 An engine of mass 5000 kg pulls a train of ten trucks each of mass 2000 kg along a horizontal track. Assume the frictional forces amount to 5000 N and that the engine exerts a force of 50 000 N on the rails. If the trucks are numbered from 1 to 10 starting with the one next to the engine, calculate:
   (a) the net total accelerating force [2]
   (b) the acceleration of the train [1]
   (c) the force of truck 6 on truck 7 [2]
   (d) the force of truck 9 on truck 8 [2]

7 A heavy ball with a mass of 5 kg is thrown with a velocity of $6 \, \text{m s}^{-1}$ to a boy who is standing on a skateboard at rest. He catches it and as a result moves backwards at $0.5 \, \text{m s}^{-1}$. What is the combined mass $(m)$ of the boy and skateboard? [3]

8 Two bodies, P and Q, of equal mass move towards each other at speeds $u$ and $v$ respectively. They make an elastic collision, and during the collision P is momentarily at rest. What is the speed of Q at that moment?
   A   $v - u$
   B   $2(v - u)$
   C   zero
   D   $\sqrt{uv}$ [1]

9 A firework rocket moves upwards and then explodes into two unequal fragments at the top of its flight path. They both move horizontally immediately after the explosion, one moves to the left at $25 \, \text{m s}^{-1}$ and the other to the right at $75 \, \text{m s}^{-1}$.
   (a) If the mass of the fragment moving to the left is 800 g what is the mass of the other fragment? [3]
   (b) What is the kinetic energy of the fragment moving left immediately after the explosion? [2]
   (c) What is the kinetic energy of the other fragment immediately after the explosion? [2]
   (d) Why is it necessary that the two fragments initially move off in exactly opposite directions? [2]

10 A car of mass $m$ has an engine that can produce a power $P$. What is the minimum time in which the car can be accelerated from rest to a speed $v$?
   A   $\dfrac{mv^2}{P}$
   B   $\dfrac{2P}{mv^2}$
   C   $\dfrac{mv^2}{2P}$
   D   $\dfrac{mv^2}{4P}$ [1]

11 A load of 50 kg is lifted by a small crane that is 35% efficient. If the load rises 6 m in 3 seconds, calculate the power used by the crane. [2]

12 A monofilament nylon fishing line of original length 1.5 m and diameter 0.75 mm extends by 4 cm when a certain load is applied. (Young modulus for the fishing line = $6.5 \times 10^9 \, \text{Pa}$)
   (a) Calculate the elastic energy stored in the line. [2]
   (b) The fishing line mentioned in part (a) will support a load of 100 N if it is applied steadily but will break when the same load is applied to it sharply. Why is this? [2]

13 A steel wire of diameter $d$ has a strain of $12.0 \times 10^{-4}$ when supporting a certain load. If the wire is replaced by a second wire of the same material, but with a diameter of $d/2$, what will be the strain in this wire if it supports the same load?

A $6.0 \times 10^{-3}$

B $4.8 \times 10^{-3}$

C $2.4 \times 10^{-3}$

D $6.0 \times 10^{-4}$ [1]

14 The gravitational field strength at the surface of a neutron star is $1.35 \times 10^{12}\,\text{N kg}^{-1}$.

What would be the theoretical maximum height of a cylindrical granite column that could support its own weight without crushing when exposed to a field of this magnitude? (density of granite = $2700\,\text{kg m}^{-3}$; crushing strength = $3.6 \times 10^{6}\,\text{Pa}$) [2]

## Answers and quick quiz 4 online

ONLINE

## Summary

You should now have an understanding of:
- scalars and vectors — scalar quantities have only magnitude, while vector quantities have both magnitude and direction
- moments — the turning effect of a force about a point; moment = force × perpendicular distance from the point to the line of action of the force; for a body to be in equilibrium, both the resultant force and the resultant moment must be zero
- motion along a straight line — governed by the equations of motion for uniform acceleration
- projectile motion — this can be considered in two parts, one horizontal (uniform motion) and one vertical (accelerated motion)
- Newton's laws of motion — the first law governs the motion of bodies under no resultant force; the second is concerned with their behaviour with a resultant force; and the third explains the action of forces on two bodies
- momentum — mass × velocity; momentum is conserved in all collisions
- work, power (the rate at which work is done), energy and efficiency
- conservation of energy — energy is not created or destroyed but can be changed from one form to another
- density — mass/volume
- Hooke's law — the force is directly proportional to the extension up to the elastic limit
- the Young modulus — $(F/A)/(\Delta L/L)$; this is the modulus of elasticity that governs the linear extension of a specimen when a force is applied

# 5 Electricity

## Basics of electricity

### Electric charge

When an electric current flows, electrical energy is converted to other forms of energy such as heat, light, chemical, magnetic and so on.

In a metal there is a large number of electrons that are not held around particular nuclei but are free to move at high speed and in a random way through the metal. These are known are **free electrons** and in a metal there are always large numbers of these. It is when these free electrons are all made to move in a certain direction by the application of a voltage across the metal that we have an electric current (Figure 5.1).

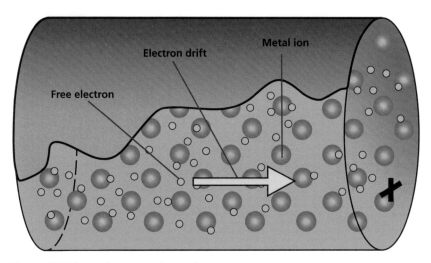

**Figure 5.1 Free electrons in a wire**

Each electron has only a very small amount of electric charge ($e$), so a larger unit is used when measuring practical units of charge. This unit is the **coulomb**:

1 coulomb = $-6.25 \times 10^{18} e$

Therefore the charge on one electron is $-1.6 \times 10^{-19}$ C.

### Electric current as a rate of flow of charge

A **current** of 1A flows in a wire if a charge of 1C passes any point in the wire each second.

The rate of flow of electric **charge** ($\Delta Q/\Delta t$) round a circuit is the electric current in that circuit.

**Typical mistake**

Not using seconds for the time when calculating current.

### Example 1

Calculate the current in a wire if a charge of 240 C passes a given point in 3 minutes.

Answer

$$\text{current} = \frac{Q}{t} = \frac{240}{180} = 1.33\,\text{A}$$

### Example 2

A current of 25 mA flows for 10 ms.
(a) What charge has passed?
(b) How many electrons have flowed past that point in the circuit.

Answer

(a) charge = current × time = 0.025 × 0.010 = 0.00025 C = $2.5 \times 10^{-4}$ C

(b) number of electrons $= \dfrac{2.5 \times 10^{-4}}{1.6 \times 10^{-19}} = 1.56 \times 10^{15}$

## Now test yourself

TESTED

1 (a) A charge of 20 C passes a point in a circuit in 4 s. What is the current in the circuit? (Give your answer in amps.)
  (b) A charge of 600 C passes a point in a circuit in 20 minutes. What is the current in the circuit? (Give your answer in milliamps.)
2 (a) A current of 2 A flows for 10 s. What charge has passed? (Give your answer in coulombs.)
  (b) A current of 5 mA flows for 8 minutes. What charge has passed? (Give your answer in coulombs.)

Answers on p. 116

Note that we are using the conventional direction for electric current flow, i.e from positive to negative. In actual fact, of course, the electrons in a wire move from negative to positive when a current flows.

## Resistance

REVISED

As the free electrons in an electric current move through the metal they collide with each other and with the atoms of the metal. These collisions impede their movement and this property of the material is called its **resistance**.

The **resistance** (R) of a given piece of material is connected to the current flowing through it (I) and the potential difference (V) between its ends by the equation:

$$\text{resistance} = \frac{\textbf{potential difference}}{\textbf{current}}$$

$$R = \frac{V}{I}$$

## Potential difference

As a charge moves round a circuit from the positive to the negative it loses energy.

> **The electrical potential energy of a unit charge at a point in a circuit is called the potential at that point.**

The difference in electrical potential between two points in the circuit is known as the **potential difference** between those two places.

---

**Potential difference** between two points in a circuit is the work done ($W$) in moving unit charge ($Q$) (i.e. 1 coulomb) from one point to the other:

$$\text{potential difference, } V = \frac{\Delta W}{\Delta Q}$$

The units for both potential and potential difference are joules per coulomb, or volts (1 volt = 1 joule per coulomb).

---

# Current–voltage characteristics

## Ohm's law

If the ratio of $V$ to $I$ remains constant for a series of different potential differences the material is said to obey Ohm's law and is known as an **ohmic conductor**.

This means that although we can always work out the resistance of a sample, knowing the current through it and the p.d. across it, if these quantities are altered we can only *predict* how it will behave under these new conditions if it obeys **Ohm's law**.

---

**Ohm's law** states that the current in a conductor is directly proportional to the potential difference across it.

---

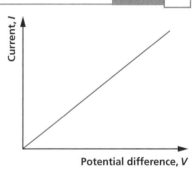

**Figure 5.2** Ohm's law graph

Figure 5.2 shows the variation of current ($I$) with potential difference ($V$) for a material that obeys Ohm's law — in other words, an ohmic conductor.

It is important to realise that Ohm's Law only holds for a *metallic conductor* at a *constant temperature*.

Figure 5.3 shows the variation in the potential around the circuit. We can follow this by considering each section of the circuit in turn.
- Along the connecting wire from the cell to B there is no resistance and so no loss of electrical energy or drop in potential.
- In the resistors $r$ and $R$ energy is converted to heat and so the potential drops from B through to E.
- From E to the cell there is no loss of electrical energy and so the potential at E is the same as that at the negative terminal of the cell — zero.

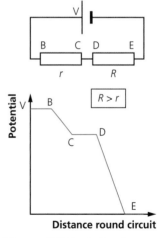

**Figure 5.3** Variation in potential round a circuit

---

**Example 1**

A 6 V battery is connected to a small electromagnet and a current of 1.5 A flows through it. What is the resistance of the electromagnet?

**Answer**

$$\text{resistance} = \frac{\text{voltage}}{\text{current}} = \frac{6}{1.5} = 4\,\Omega$$

---

> ### Example 2
>
> A current of 0.5 mA flows through a resistor of 100 kΩ. What is the potential difference across the resistor?
>
> Answer
>
> voltage = current × resistance = 0.0005 × 100 000 = 50 V

## Now test yourself

3 Calculate the current through the following resistors:
  (a) 120 Ω connected to 200 mV
  (b) 4700 Ω connected to 12 V
  (c) 10 kΩ connected to 6 V
  (d) 2.5 MΩ connected to 25 V
4 What is the resistance of the following?
  (a) a torch bulb that draws 0.25 A from a 12 V supply
  (b) an immersion heater that draws 10 A from a 230 V supply

Answers on p. 116

# Common current–voltage characteristics

A current sensor and a voltage sensor can be used to capture data to give *V–I* curves. Figure 5.4 shows some common examples.

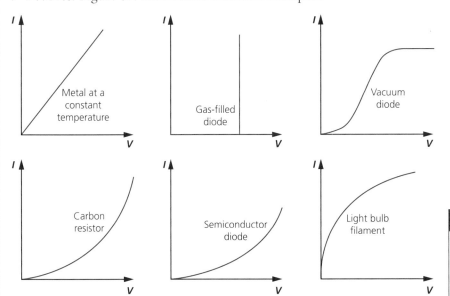

Figure 5.4 Common *I–V* curves

> ### Typical mistake
>
> Using the gradient of a *V–I* curve for a non-ohmic conductor to calculate resistance.

The graph for a metal at a constant temperature is an example of an ohmic conductor (see below).

# Resistivity

## What is resistivity?

There are three factors that affect the resistance of a sample of a material:
● the temperature
● the dimensions of the sample — the smaller the cross-sectional area and the longer the sample the larger the resistance
● the material from which the sample is made

Exam practice answers and quick quizzes at **www.hoddereducation.co.uk/myrevisionnotes**

The property of the material that affects its resistance is called the **resistivity** of the material (Figure 5.5), symbol $\rho$.

---

The **resistivity** of a material is defined as the resistance between two opposite faces of a metre cube of the material. It is related to the resistance ($R$) of a specimen of length $L$ and cross-sectional area $A$ by the formula:

$$\text{resistivity, } \rho = \frac{RA}{L}$$

The units for resistivity are $\Omega\,\text{m}$.

---

**Typical mistake**

Using $\Omega\,\text{m}^{-1}$ instead of $\Omega\,\text{m}$ as the unit for resistivity.

---

**Resistance, R**

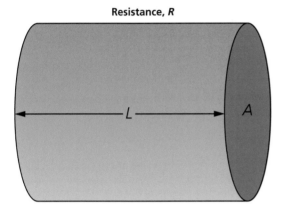

**Figure 5.5 Resistivity definition**

The resistivities of good conductors are very small numbers (usually between $10^{-8}$ and $10^{-6}\,\Omega\,\text{m}$), rising to around $1\,\Omega\,\text{m}$ for semiconductors and $10^{15}\,\Omega\,\text{m}$ for 'insulators'.

---

**Example 1**

Calculate the resistance of a 1.5 m long piece of wire of resistivity $30 \times 10^{-8}\,\Omega\,\text{m}$ and diameter 0.5 mm.

Answer

$$\text{resistance} = \frac{\text{resistivity} \times \text{length}}{\text{area}} = \frac{30 \times 10^{-8} \times 1.5}{1.96 \times 10^{-7}} = 2.3\,\Omega$$

---

**Example 2**

Some resistance wire (resistivity $40 \times 10^{-8}\,\Omega\,\text{m}$) is used to make a heater. The wire on the reel has a cross-sectional area of $1.5 \times 10^{-7}\,\text{m}^2$, and the required resistance is $5\,\Omega$. What length of wire is needed?

Answer

$$\text{length} = \frac{\text{resistance} \times \text{area}}{\text{resistivity}} = \frac{5 \times 1.5 \times 10^{-7}}{40 \times 10^{-8}} = 1.88\,\text{m}$$

---

**Exam tip**

In resistivity calculations make sure that you use metres and not cm or mm, and radius and not diameter.

## Required practical 5

### Measurement of resistivity

The resistivity of a wire can be measured using a low-voltage power supply, a micrometer, an ammeter and a voltmeter.

- First measure the diameter of the wire in a number of places using the micrometer and calculate an average value.
- Then connect the wire and meters to the power supply and apply a small voltage.
- Take readings of the current through the wire and the potential difference across it.
- Hence calculate the resistivity.

It is important to avoid heating the wire by using too large a potential difference.

An alternative method uses an ohm meter instead of the ammeter, voltmeter and power supply.

## Now test yourself

TESTED

5  Calculate the resistivity of a material if a 250 cm length of wire of that material with a diameter of 0.56 mm has a resistance of 3 Ω.

6  Calculate the resistance between the large faces of a slab of germanium of thickness 1 mm and area 1.5 mm². The resistivity of germanium is 0.65 Ωm.

Answers on p. 116

## Resistance and temperature

REVISED

When a material is heated its resistivity will change and therefore so will the resistance of a specimen of that material. The nature of the change depends on the material. The change is governed by a property called the **temperature coefficient of resistance** ($\alpha$). This is positive for metals but negative for non–metals such as semiconductors.

### Metals

For a metal an increase in the temperature gives an increase in resistance. At low temperatures the thermal vibration of the lattice ions is small and electrons can move easily, but at high temperatures the motion increases, giving a much greater chance of collisions between the conduction electrons and the lattice ions, so impeding their motion.

The variation is shown in Figure 5.6.

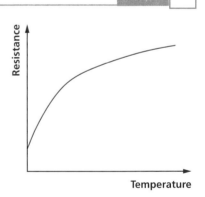

Figure 5.6 Metal resistance and temperature variation

## Semiconductors

In semiconductors an increase in temperature leads to a drop in resistance. Bound electrons gain energy and move into the conduction band, resulting in an increase in the number of free electrons. The temperature coefficient of resistance is therefore negative. Such materials are called negative temperature coefficient (NTC) semiconductors.

## Thermistors

The change of resistance of a semiconductor with temperature is used in temperature sensitive resistors called thermistors. The most widely used are NTC thermistors whose resistance falls as the temperature rises. The symbol for a thermistor and a graph of the variation of its resistance with temperature are shown in Figure 5.7.

Thermistors are used as temperature sensors in thermostats in ovens and irons, in fire alarms and on the wing of a plane to detect when the temperature falls low enough for ice to form. They are also in use in premature baby units to detect when a baby may have stopped breathing, current-limiting devices and thermometers.

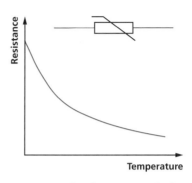

**Figure 5.7 Resistance variation for an NTC thermistor**

### Now test yourself

TESTED

7 When is the filament in a 'traditional' light bulb most likely to break? Explain your answer.

Answer on p. 116

## Superconductivity

REVISED

When metals cool, their resistance falls steadily as the motion of the atoms of the metal and the free electrons gets less and so the number of electron–atom collisions is reduced.

However, it was found that as the metal is cooled further a temperature can be reached where the resistance suddenly falls to zero — when this happens the metal is said to be **superconducting** and the phenomenon is called **superconductivity**.

The temperature at which this happens for a given metal is called the **critical temperature** for the metal.

The importance of superconductivity is that if a material is superconducting it has no resistance, this means that an electric current can flow through it without energy loss in the form of resistive heating.

Applications of superconductivity include:
● high-power superconducting electromagnets for use in both the levitation of experimental trains and in nuclear accelerators
● superconducting power cables for electrical energy transmission

# Circuits

## Resistors in series

A series circuit is one where the components are connected one after the other. This means that the current passing through all the components is the same.

In Figure 5.8 the current through both resistors is $I$ and the potential difference across $R_1$ is $V_1$ and that across $R_2$ is $V_2$.

The total resistance $(R)$ of a set of resistors in series is simply found by adding the values of the resistance of each resistor together:

$$R = R_1 + R_2 + R_3 + ...$$

The above formula is true no matter how many resistors you add.

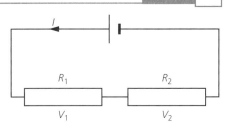

**Figure 5.8 Resistors in series**

## Resistors in parallel

When the resistors are connected in parallel the current splits at the junction, a current $I_1$ passing through $R_1$ and a current $I_2$ passing through $R_2$. The potential difference across any number of resistances connected in parallel is the same for all the resistors (Figure 5.9).

The formula for total resistance $(R)$ for resistors connected in parallel is:

$$\frac{1}{R} = \frac{1}{R_1} + \frac{1}{R_2} + \frac{1}{R_3} + ...$$

This version of the formula is true no matter how many resistors you add. However, a simpler version can be derived for two resistors in parallel:

$$R = \frac{R_1 R_2}{R_1 + R_2}$$

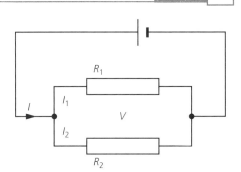

**Figure 5.9 Resistors in parallel**

> **Exam tip**
>
> The version in this form is only correct for two resistors.

---

**Example 1**

Calculate the resistance of the following combinations:
(a) $200\,\Omega$ and $100\,\Omega$ in series
(b) $200\,\Omega$ and $100\,\Omega$ in parallel.

Answer

(a) $R = R_1 + R_2 = 200 + 100 = 300\,\Omega$

(b) $\frac{1}{R} = \frac{1}{R_1} + \frac{1}{R_2} = \frac{1}{200} + \frac{1}{100} = \frac{3}{200}$ and so $R = 67\,\Omega$

> **Typical mistake**
>
> When calculating the final resistance for a pair of resistors in parallel, working out $1/R$ and then forgetting to invert it to obtain the final resistance $R$.

---

**Example 2**

You are given one $100\,\Omega$ resistor and two $50\,\Omega$ resistors. How would you connect any combination of them to give a combined resistance of:
(a) $200\,\Omega$
(b) $125\,\Omega$?

Answer

(a) $100\,\Omega$ in series with both the $50\,\Omega$
(b) the two $50\,\Omega$ in parallel and this in series with the $100\,\Omega$

## Now test yourself

8 What is the final resistance of each of the six circuits in Figure 5.10?

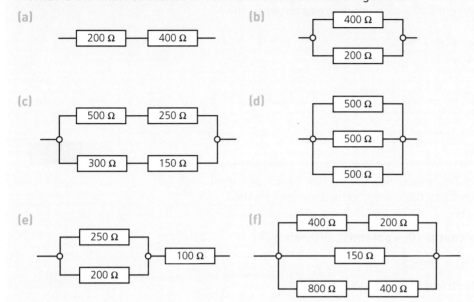

Figure 5.10

9 Figure 5.11 shows an LDR connected in parallel with a resistor and a 6 V cell of negligible internal resistance. The resistance of the LDR falls as the intensity of light falling on it is increased.

(a) Calculate the current flowing from the cell when the resistance of the LDR is 150 kΩ.

(b) What happens to this current if the light intensity is reduced?

(c) What is the minimum current that can be drawn from the cell?

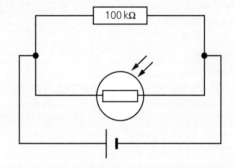

Figure 5.11 **LDR and resistor in parallel**

Answers on p. 116

# Cells in series and parallel

For cells connected in series (Figure 5.12), the total potential difference between the ends of the chain is the sum of the potential differences across each cell.

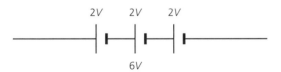

Figure 5.12 Cells in series

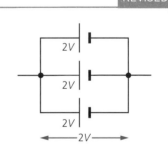

Figure 5.13 Cells in parallel

For cells connected in parallel (Figure 5.13), the total potential difference across the arrangement is the same as for one cell.

The advantage of the parallel circuit is that although the output voltage is the same as that of a single cell the battery formed from the group of cells contains more energy and so will supply current for longer.

**Typical mistake**

Not allowing for the change in total output voltage if one or more of the cells in a series is reversed.

Now test yourself

TESTED

10 You are given two 6V cells of negligible internal resistance and a
200 Ω resistor. What current flows through the resistor when the
cells are connected
(a) to the resistor in parallel
(b) to the resistor in series?

Answer on p. 116

## Electrical energy

REVISED

If a charge $Q$ moves between two points in a circuit that have a potential
difference of $V$ volts between them the energy gained (or lost) by the
charge is given by the formula:

**electrical energy = charge ($Q$) × potential difference ($V$)**

Since charge ($Q$) = current ($I$) × time ($t$):

**electrical energy = $IVt$**

Large amounts of energy are used in a car starter motor to 'turn the
engine over'. Although the voltage is low (12 V) the current required may
be a great as 200 A.

### Example

Calculate the amount of energy supplied by a 6V battery when:
(a) a charge of 25 C passes through it
(b) a current of 30 mA flows through it for 5 minutes

Answer

(a) energy = potential difference × charge = 6 × 25 = 150 J
(b) energy = potential difference × charge
= potential difference × current × time
= 6 × 30 × 10$^{-3}$ × 300 = 54 J

### Typical mistake

Forgetting to convert to SI
units, for example mA to A
and minutes to seconds.

Now test yourself

TESTED

11 Calculate how much electrical energy is supplied by a 1.5 V battery
when:
(a) a charge of 3000 C passes through it
(b) a current of 200 µA flows from it for 2.5 hours
12 How much energy is drawn from a 12 V car battery if it is used to
supply 200 A for 1.5 s to the starter motor?

Answers on p. 116

# Electrical power

**Power** is the rate at which work is done or energy changed from one form to another, and so:

$$\text{electrical power} = \frac{\text{energy}}{\text{time}} = \frac{VQ}{t} = VI$$

Electrical power is measured in watts (W) where $1\,\text{W} = 1\,\text{J}\,\text{s}^{-1}$. For large power outputs we use kilowatts ($1\,\text{kW} = 1000\,\text{W}$) and megawatts ($1\,\text{MW} = 1\,000\,000\text{W}$).

Since $V = IR$, and power $= VI$:

$$\text{electrical power} = VI = I^2R = \frac{V^2}{R}$$

## Example 1

Calculate the current used by a 12V immersion heater that is designed to deliver 30 000 J in 5 minutes.

Answer

energy = power × time = 30 000

Therefore:

30 000 = power × 300

power = 100 W

So:

$$\text{current} = \frac{100}{12} = 8.3\,\text{A}$$

## Example 2

(a) Calculate the resistance of a 100W light bulb if it takes a current of 0.8A.
(b) Calculate the power of a 12V immersion heater with a resistance of 10Ω.

Answer

(a) power $= I^2R$
Therefore $R = \dfrac{100}{0.64} = 156.3\,\Omega$

(b) power $= \dfrac{V^2}{R} = \dfrac{144}{10} = 14.4\,\text{W}$

## Now test yourself

TESTED

13 What power is supplied to the heater of an electric bar fire with a resistance of 50Ω connected to the mains 230V supply?
14 What is the power loss down a copper connecting lead 75cm long with a resistance of 0.13Ω per metre when a current of 4.5A flows through it?

Answer on p. 116

AQA AS/A-level Year 1 Physics    103

## Conservation of charge and energy

In an electrical circuit both charge and energy must be conserved. These requirements are usually expressed in Kirchhoff's two rules:

1 **The algebraic sum of the currents at a junction is zero. In other words there is no build up of charge at a junction ($\Sigma I = 0$).**
2 **The sum of the changes in potential round a closed circuit must be zero.**

Rule 1 is about charge conservation while rule 2 is about energy conservation (Figure 5.14).

Rule 1 — at point B there is a junction:

current flowing from the cell ($I$) = Current in $R_1$ ($I_1$) + current in $R_2$ ($I_2$)

Rule 2 — round loop A–B–C–D–E:

p.d. across cell $= -$ p.d. across $R_1$

This represents a gain of potential in the cell but a loss in $R_1$.

In this equation there is a minus because we are moving 'against' the current in $R_2$.

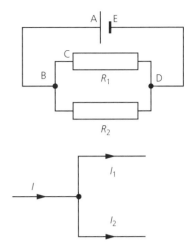

**Figure 5.14 Conservation of charge and energy**

### Example

Consider the circuit in Figure 5.15.

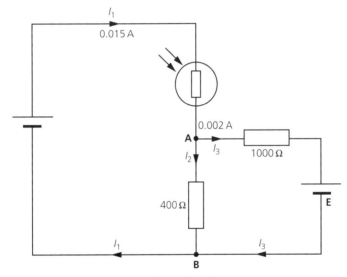

Figure 5.15 **Example problem circuit**

Applying Kirchhoff's first rule to junction A:

current in the 400 Ω resistor = 0.015 – 0.002 = 0.013 A

potential difference across 400 Ω resistor = 0.013 × 400 = 5.2 V

This is the potential difference between A and B via the 400 Ω resistor but it is also the potential difference across the right-hand branch of the circuit via the cell of emf ε (p. 109).

The potential drop across the 1000 Ω resistor is 0.002 × 1000 = 2 V.

Applying Kirchhoff's second rule to the right-hand branch and considering an anticlockwise direction from the cell:

EMF of the cell, $E$ = (–0.002 x 1000) + 5.2 = –2 + 5.2 = 3.2 V

The minus sign is there because the current in the 1000 Ω resistor is travelling in the opposite direction from that in which the emf of the cell is acting.

TESTED

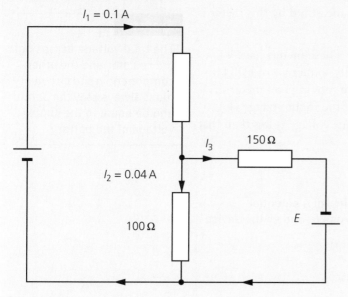

Figure 5.16

15 Using Figure 5.16:
   (a) Find the magnitude and direction of $I_3$.
   (b) Find the magnitude and direction of $E$.
16 Using Figure 5.16:
   (a) If $I_1 = 0.2\,A$ and $I_2 = 0.5\,A$, find the magnitude and direction of $I_3$.
   (b) If $I_1 = 0.3\,A$ and $I_2 = 0.1\,A$, find the magnitude and direction of $I_3$.

Answers on p. 116

# Potential dividers

## Basic circuit

REVISED

Two resistors connected across a cell enable the output of the cell to be divided between them. Such a circuit is called a potential divider. The basic circuit is shown in Figure 5.17. If the output is continuously variable from 0 to $V$ the device is known as a potentiometer. The p.d. across $R_1$ and $R_2$ is fixed ($V$). The output voltage across AB is given by:

$$\text{output voltage, } V_2 = \frac{R_2}{(R_1 + R_2)}V$$

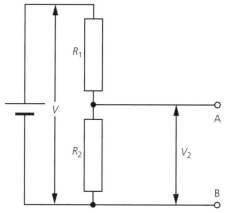

Figure 5.17 Potential divider circuit

> **Typical mistake**
>
> Taking the ratio of the two resistors rather than the ratio of one resistor to the sum of both.

## Measuring the output voltage with a meter

This can be done using a **digital voltmeter** with very high (if not virtually infinite) resistance. The output voltage measured by this meter is that across $R_2$, in other words $V_2$.

Another option is to use a **moving coil meter**. These meters have a much lower resistance than a digital meter, usually some tens of $k\Omega$. This means that the combined resistance of $R_2$ and the moving coil meter in parallel with it is less than $R_2$. The proportion of the input voltage $(V)$ dropped across $R_2$ therefore falls and so the output voltage is less than that measured with a digital meter.

### Example

A loudspeaker is connected across the output $(R_2)$ of a potential divider. Varying $R_1$ will change the potential across $R_2$ and so the device acts as a volume control (Figure 5.18).

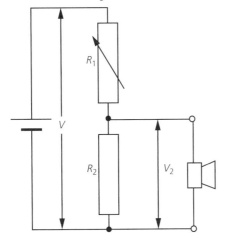

Figure 5.18 **Potential divider with loudspeaker**

If $V = 6\,V$, $R_1 = 200\,\Omega$, $R_2 = 0.5\,k\Omega$ and the loudspeaker has a resistance of $100\,\Omega$, calculate the p.d. across it.

Answer

Call the combined resistance of $R_2$ and the loudspeaker $R_3$:

$$R_3 = \frac{500 \times 100}{600} = 83\,\Omega$$

(This the resistance of $R_2$ $(500\,\Omega)$ and the loudspeaker $(100\,\Omega)$ in parallel.)

Therefore, using the formula for the potential divider:

$$V_2 = \frac{R_3}{(R_1 + R_3)} \times 6$$

p.d across the speaker, $V_2 = (83/283)6 = 1.8\,V$

## Light-dependent resistor (LDR)

An LDR is a component that has a resistance that changes when light falls on it. As the intensity of the light is increased, so the resistance of the LDR falls.

If the LDR is connected as part of a potential divider, as shown in Figure 5.19, then as the light level is increased its resistance falls and the proportion of the input voltage dropped across it will also fall.

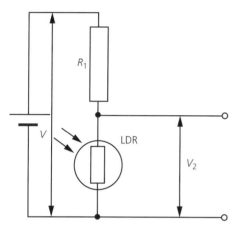

Figure 5.19 Potential divider with LDR

So in the light $V_2$ is low and in the dark $V_2$ is high.

## Thermistor

If $R_2$ is replaced by an NTC thermistor the circuit is temperature dependent. As the temperature of the thermistor rises its resistance falls and so the voltage dropped across it falls.

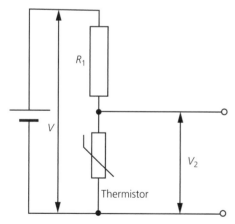

Figure 5.20 Potential divider with a thermistor

When the thermistor is hot $V_2$ is low and when the thermistor is cold $V_2$ is high.

Both these examples have considered $R_2$ being replaced by another component. If $R_1$ is replaced then if the voltage across this component rises the output voltage across $R_2$ will fall.

> **Revision activity**
>
> Make a mind map showing the various possible circuits using a potential divider (e.g resistors, thermistor and LDR). Summarise the effect on the output p.d. of changing the values of the components.

17 Using Figure 5.17, calculate the output voltage for the following values of $V$, $R_1$ and $R_2$.
   (a) $V = 12\,V$, $R_1 = 100\,k\Omega$, $R_2 = 200\,k\Omega$
   (b) $V = 10\,V$, $R_1 = 25\,k\Omega$, $R_2 = 20\,k\Omega$
   (c) $V = 6\,V$, $R_1 = 250\,\Omega$, $R_2 = 200\,\Omega$
18 (a) Resistor $R_1$ is now replaced by a thermistor with a negative temperature coefficient — one where the resistance decreases as the temperature rises.
   If the values of the resistance of $R_2$ and the thermistor are equal at the start, what will happen to the output potential difference ($V$) as the thermistor is cooled?
   (b) Resistor $R_2$ is now replaced by a light-dependent resistor. ($R_1$ is a fixed resistor.)
   If the values of the resistance of $R_1$ and the LDR are equal at the start, what will happen to the output potential difference ($V$) as the intensity of the light falling on the LDR is decreased?

Answers on p. 116

## The variable resistor as a potential divider

REVISED

Another way of varying the output potential difference is to use a variable resistor or rheostat (Figure 5.21). This is made of a length wire wrapped round a former.

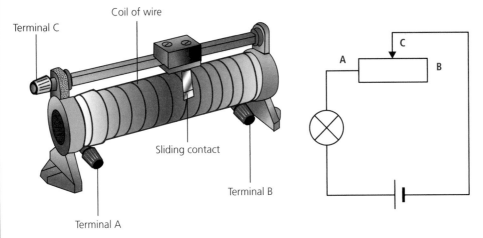

Figure 5.21 **The variable resistor**

The source potential is connected between A and B and the output taken between B and C.

# Electromotive force and internal resistance

## Electromotive force

When a charge passes through a cell it gains energy. The energy gained per coulomb in the cell is called the **electromotive force (emf)** ($\varepsilon$). It is the energy delivered per coulomb by the cell and so:

$$\text{Electromotive force } (\varepsilon) = \frac{E}{Q}$$

When a current flows from the cell energy may be converted to other forms within the cell and the potential difference ($V$) between the terminals of the cell will then be less than the emf of the cell.

Note that emf is not a force. It is energy per unit charge, in other words a voltage.

> The **emf** ($\varepsilon$) of the cell is the maximum potential difference that the cell can produce across its terminals, or the open circuit potential difference.

## Internal resistance

All cells have a resistance of their own and we call this the **internal resistance** ($r$) of the cell. The loss of electrical energy within the cell and the resulting reduction in the output potential difference is due to this internal resistance.

The internal resistance is related to the emf by the following equation:

$$\varepsilon = \frac{E}{Q} = V + Ir = I(R + r)$$

where $I$ is the current flowing through the cell.

Figure 5.22 explains the ideas of emf and internal resistance.

The shaded area represents the internal part of the cell.

The quantity of useful electrical energy available outside the cell is $IR$ and $Ir$ is the energy transformed to other forms within the cell itself.

We usually require the internal resistance of a cell to be small to reduce the electrical energy transformed within the cell. The low internal resistance of a car battery allows it to deliver large currents without a large amount of electrical energy being converted to other forms within the battery itself. However it is sometimes helpful to have a rather larger internal resistance to prevent large currents from flowing if the cell terminals are shorted.

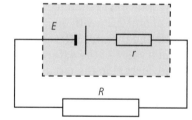

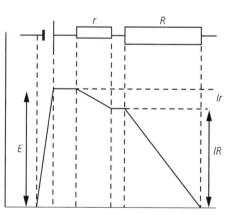

**Figure 5.22 Emf and internal resistance**

## Example

A cell of emf 12V and internal resistance $0.2\,\Omega$ is used in two circuits. Calculate the potential difference between its terminals when it is connected to:

(a) $15\,\Omega$

(b) $0.1\,\Omega$.

Answer

(a) total resistance $= 15 + 0.2 = 15.2\,\Omega$

Therefore:

current $= \dfrac{12}{15.2} = 0.789\,A$

'loss' of energy per coulomb in the cell $= 0.789 \times 0.2 = 0.158\,V$

potential difference between terminals $= 12 - 0.158 = 11.84\,V$

(b) total resistance $= 0.2 + 0.1 = 0.3\,\Omega$

Therefore:

current $= \dfrac{12}{0.3} = 40\,A$

'loss' of energy per coulomb in the cell $= 40 \times 0.1 = 4\,V$

potential difference between terminals $= 12 - 4 = 8\,V$

### Exam tip

The word 'loss' is used here, although it should really be replaced with 'electrical energy converted to other forms'.

## Now test yourself

TESTED

19 Explain what happens to the output potential across the terminals of a cell with some internal resistance as the current from it is increased.

20 A digital voltmeter with resistance of $10\,M\Omega$ reads 1.30V when connected across the terminals of a cell. When the same meter is connected across a resistor of $20\,\Omega$ that has been connected in series with the cell the voltmeter reads 1.25V.

Explain the difference between these two readings and calculate:

(a) the current in the external resistor

(b) the internal resistance of the cell.

21 A cell of emf 2.5V with an internal resistance of $0.15\,\Omega$ is connected in turn to external resistors of

(a) $20\,\Omega$ and then (b) $1\,\Omega$.

For each value of the external resistor calculate:

(i) the current in the circuit

(ii) the potential difference across the terminals of the cell

(iii) the power loss inside the cell.

Answers on p. 116–117

## Required practical 6

### Investigation of the emf and internal resistance of electric cells

The emf ($\varepsilon$) of a cell can be measured using a high-resistance voltmeter connected between its terminals. The high resistance means that there is effectively zero current being drawn from the cell. The internal resistance can be found by connecting a variable resistor between the terminals of the cell and measuring the p.d. across it for a range of resistances ($R$). The intercept of the line on the $I$ axis of a graph of $I$

against $R$ will give the internal resistance of the cell ($r = \dfrac{\varepsilon}{I}$).

# Exam practice

1 (a) Figure 5.23 shows the variation of current with voltage for a metal wire at two different temperatures.

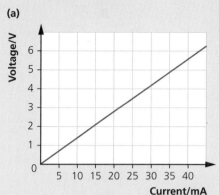

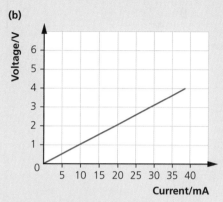

**Figure 5.23 Voltage–current variation at different temperatures**

    (i) Calculate the resistance of the wire at each temperature.    [2]
    (ii) Which graph shows the higher temperature?    [1]
(b) (i) What is the resistance of the component at the point marked A on the graph in Figure 5.24?    [2]

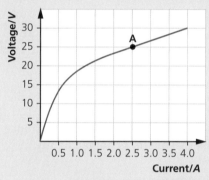

**Figure 5.24 Voltage–current variation for a component**

    (ii) Does the material disobey Ohm's law? Explain your answer.    [2]

2 (a) What is the resistance between the points A and B of the combination of resistors shown in Figure 5.25?    [2]
(b) Explain how you arrived at the answer.    [4]

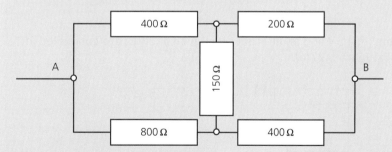

**Figure 5.25 Resistance network**

3 You are given four resistors, 20 kΩ, 10 kΩ, 5 kΩ and 1 kΩ. How would you connect two or more of them to make the following total resistances?
  (a) 15 kΩ    [1]
  (b) 14 kΩ    [2]
  (c) 6.67 kΩ    [2]
  (d) 4.33 kΩ    [2]

4 A current $I$ flows though a wire of length $L$ and radius of cross-section $r$, which is made of material of resistivity $\rho$.

The rate of heat generation in the wire is:

A $\dfrac{IL\rho}{r}$      B $\dfrac{I^2L\rho}{\pi r^2}$      C $\left[\dfrac{L\rho}{\pi r^2}\right]^2$      D $\dfrac{\pi r^2}{I\rho L}$    [1]

5 A potential divider is set up as shown in Figure 5.26.

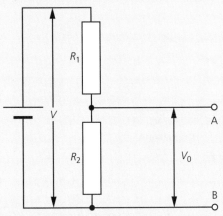

**Figure 5.26 Potential divider circuit**

The emf of the cell is 6 V and the values of $R_1$ and $R_2$ are 200 Ω and 400 Ω respectively. A digital voltmeter of very high resistance (>10 MΩ) connected between A and B is used to measure the output voltage ($V_o$).

(a) Calculate the output voltage. [2]

(b) If the digital voltmeter is replaced with an analogue meter of resistance 1000 Ω calculate the new output voltage. Explain your answer. [3]

(c) The digital voltmeter is replaced and $R_1$ is replaced by an NTC thermistor of initial resistance 200 Ω. Explain what happens to the output voltage when the thermistor is heated gently. [2]

6 (a) What is the definition of a volt? [1]

(b) What is the definition of electromotive force (emf)? [1]

(c) What is meant by internal resistance? [1]

(d) Why is internal resistance of a source a useful safety factor? [2]

7 A low-voltage school power supply has an emf of 12 V and internal resistance of 3 Ω. Calculate the currents drawn from the power supply and the values of the output voltage when the power supply is connected to:

(a) a resistor of 25 Ω [2]

(b) a resistor of 2.5 Ω. [1]

(c) Explain your answers. [2]

8 Three identical cells, each with an emf of 1.5 V and an internal resistance of 2.0 Ω, are connected in series to a 4.0 Ω resistor, as shown in Figure 5.27 (a).

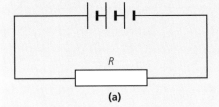 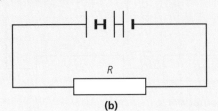

(a)                  (b)

**Figure 5.27**

If one of the cells is reversed (Figure 5.27(b)) what is the ratio of the power output in $R$ in circuit (a) to the power output in $R$ in circuit (b)?

A   3.0
B   5.4
C   7.2
D   9.0

[1]

## Answers and quick quiz 5 online

ONLINE

## Summary

You should now have an understanding of:
- the basics of electricity — this to include charge and current as a flow of charge, resistance and Ohm's law and the variation of current with voltage for a number of circuits
- current–voltage characteristics — various versions of these curves can be found in Figure 5.4 (p. 96)
- resistivity ($\rho$) — this is a property of the material and not a particular specimen; resisitivity = resistance × area/length (units $\Omega$ m)

- resistance and temperature — how the resistance of resistors and thermistors changes with temperature
- circuits — combinations of resistors in series and parallel, and their associated formulae
- potential divider circuits — the use of two or more resistors to give a fractional output of the applied p.d.
- electromotive force and internal resistance — the emf ($\varepsilon$) of the cell is the maximum potential difference that the cell can produce across its terminals; the output potential difference is less due to the internal resistance of the cell

# Now test yourself answers

## Chapter 1

1  $0.000025\,J = 2.5 \times 10^{-4}\,J$

2  $\text{pressure} = \dfrac{\text{force}}{\text{area}} = \dfrac{\text{mass} \times \text{acceleration}}{\text{area}} =$
    $kg\,m\,s^{-2}/m^2 = kg\,m^{-1}\,s^{-2}$

## Chapter 2

1  (a) 143
   (b) 146

2  54

3  (a) $^{14}_{7}N$
   (b) $^{14}_{6}C \rightarrow {}^{14}_{7}N + {}^{0}_{-1}e + \bar{\nu}_e$

4  (a) alpha
   (b) $^{238}_{92}U \rightarrow {}^{234}_{90}Th + {}^{4}_{2}He$

5  (a) $2 \times 10^{-13}\,J$
   (b) $2 \times 10^{-15}\,J$
   (c) $4.74 \times 10^{-19}\,J$
   (d) $3.32 \times 10^{-19}\,J$
   (e) $2.84 \times 10^{-19}\,J$
   (f) $9.95 \times 10^{-24}\,J$
   (g) $7.83 \times 10^{-28}\,J$

6  Charge: $-1 = +1 + 0 + 0$
   Lepton number: $1 = 1 + 1 + (-1)$

7  $1.33 \times 10^{-18}\,J$

8  (a) $1.66 \times 10^{-18}\,J$
   (b) $1.0 \times 10^{-18}\,J$
   (c) $1.5 \times 10^{15}\,Hz$

9  $\text{frequency} = \dfrac{E_2 - E_1}{h} = 2.46 \times 10^{15}\,Hz$
   $\text{wavelength} = c/f = 122\,nm$

10  $\text{wavelength} = h/mv = 3.97 \times 10^{-14}\,m$
    $= 3.97 \times 10^{-5}\,nm$

## Chapter 3

1  $2.94\,m$

2  Light is electromagnetic radiation (varying electric and magnetic fields) and this will travel through a vacuum. Sound requires a medium to transmit it and so would not be transmitted though the virtually airless 'atmosphere' of the Moon.

3  (a) They would be aligned with the bars parallel to each other.
   (b) The received signal would vary in intensity sinusoidally.

4  half a wavelength

5  The ends of a stretched string will be fixed points.

6  The received signal is the result of the superposition of the signals from the two transmitters.
   distance between maxima $= \dfrac{\lambda}{2} = 30 \times 5 = 150\,m$; wavelength $= 300\,m$

7  (a) fringe width $= \lambda D/s$
   $= \dfrac{600 \times 10^{-9} \times 0.9}{0.5 \times 10^{-3}} = 0.108\,mm$
   (b) moved further away by 18 cm

8  $\text{wavelength} = \dfrac{4.5 \times 10^{-3} \times 0.6 \times 10^{-3}}{4}$
   $= 6.75 \times 10^{-7}\,m = 675\,nm$

9  Light has a much shorter wavelength.

10  Yes — sound waves show diffraction.

11  (a) $d = \dfrac{1}{250\,000} = 4 \times 10^{-6}\,m$
    $n\lambda = d\sin\theta$
    $\sin\theta = \dfrac{550 \times 10^{-9}}{4 \times 10^{-6}} = 0.1375$
    $\theta = 7.9°$
    (b) $n = \dfrac{d\sin 90}{550 \times 10^{-9}} = 7$
    (c) Seven either side of a central image (15).

12  Spectra wider because of the finer 'grating spacing'.

13  $n_1 \sin\theta_1 = n_2 \sin\theta_2$
    refractive index $(n_1) = 1.47$

14  critical angle $= \dfrac{n_d}{n_w} = 33.3°$

15  critical angle for the glass $= 42°$
    maximum angle of incidence at one face $\leq 90°$
    maximum angle of incidence at the adjacent face in the glass $= 90 - 42 = 48°$
    Therefore total internal reflection will take place at this face and so the light will not emerge.

16  Different wavelengths of light will have different refractive indices. Therefore these different wavelengths will travel at different speeds in the fibre. This will give pulse broadening.

# Chapter 4

1 bearing 8.2°; speed 353 m s$^{-1}$

2 horizontal component = 2000 cos 15 = 1932 N
vertical component = 2000 sin15 = 518 N

3 Using moment = $Fd \sin \theta$:
(a) 9.6 N m
(b) 15 N m
(c) 34 N m

4 140 = 0.225 × $F$
$F$ = 622 N

5 Take moments about P:
(1.5 × 6 × 9.8) + (3 × 8) = 112.2 = $T\cos 35$ × 2.4
$T$ = 57.1 N

6 (a) 1050 N
(b) It will be unchanged.

7 (a) 271 m
(b) 4.4 m s$^{-1}$
(c) −0.07 m s$^{-2}$

8 216 s (3 m 36 s)

9 $a = \dfrac{v^2}{2s} = \dfrac{10^{14}}{2 \times 3 \times 10^{-2}} = 1.67 \times 10^{15}$ m s$^{-2}$

10 (a) $s = \tfrac{1}{2}gt^2 = 78.4$ m
(b) $v = gt = 39.2$ m s$^{-1}$
(c) $v_{average}$ = 19.6 m s$^{-1}$

11 (a) (i) 200 m s$^{-1}$
   (ii) 200 m s$^{-1}$
(b) (i) $v = gt$ =19.6 m s$^{-1}$
   (ii) 49 m s$^{-1}$
(c) $v = \sqrt{200^2 + 49^2} = 205$ m s$^{-1}$
   $\tan \theta$ = 49/200 $\theta$ = 13.8° to the horizontal (downwards)
(d) 1500 = 0.5 × 9.8 × $t^2$
   $t$ = 17.5 s
(e) 3500 m

12 (a) 0 m s$^{-1}$
(b) 17.5 m s$^{-1}$
(c) 9.8 m s$^{-2}$ downwards
(d) −18.7 m s$^{-1}$
(e) 25.6 m s$^{-1}$ downwards at 47° to the horizontal

13 total accelerating force = 1150 + 800 = 1950 N
acceleration = $\dfrac{1950}{83}$ = 23.5 m s$^{-2}$

14 $F$ = 550 000 − 49 000 = 60 000 N
acceleration = 1.2 m s$^{-2}$ (allow for the weight of the rocket when finding the resultant force)

15 (a) net accelerating force = 8000 − 3000 = 5000 N
(b) acceleration = $\dfrac{5000}{1800}$ = 2.78 m s$^{-2}$
(c) force = $ma$ = 800 × 2.78 = 2222 N

16 impulse = $Ft$ = area below line = 10.2 N s
impulse = $m\Delta v$
mass = 2.5 kg
$\Delta v = \dfrac{10.2}{2.5}$ = 4.1 m s$^{-1}$

17 Using momentum before collision = momentum after collision:
(0.200 × 8) + (1.5 × 0) = 1.7$v$, so 1.6 = 1.7$v$
Therefore $v$ = 0.94 m s$^{-1}$

18 (a) force = 500 cos 30 = 433 N
(b) force = 500 sin 30 = 250 N
(c) force = 433 N
work done = 433 × 40 = 17 320 J

19 (a) power = $Fv$ = 5000 × 30 = 150 kW
(b) work done = $Fs$ = 7000 × 35 = 245 000 J

20 energy change = 85 × 9.8 × 30 × 0.15 = 3750 J = 3.75 kJ

21 power = 2000 × 10$^3$ = 250 000 × 9.8 × $\dfrac{v}{10}$
Therefore, $v$ = 8.16 m s$^{-1}$

22 $M$ = 400 kg   $m$ = 70 kg
(a) $F = ma + mg = 70(a + g)$
   $s = ut + \tfrac{1}{2}at^2$
   $a = 2 \times \dfrac{5}{16} = 0.625$ m s$^{-2}$
   Therefore reading:
   $F$ = 70(9.8 + 0.625) = 70 × 10.425 = 729.75 N
(b) The reading will be constant.
(c) (i) $v^2 = u^2 + 2as$
   = 2 × 0.0.625 × 5 = 6.25 $v$ = 2.5 m s$^{-1}$
   energy = gravitational potential energy + kinetic energy = (5 × 470 × 9.8) + $\tfrac{1}{2}$(470 × 2.5$^2$)
   Therefore:
   total energy = 23 030 + 1468.75 = 24 498 J
   = 24.5 kJ
   (ii) This time there will be no kinetic energy increase.
   $s$ = 2.5 × 4 = 10 m
   Therefore:
   energy = 470 × 9.8 × 10 = 46 060 J = 46.1 kJ

23 density = $\dfrac{3 \times 10^{-6}}{3.75}$ = 8 × 10$^{-7}$ kg m$^{-3}$

24 force = 50 = 9400 × $e$
$e$ = 5.32 mm
new length = 2.50 + 0.0053 = 2.505 m

25 area = $\dfrac{\text{force}}{\text{breaking stress}} = \dfrac{30\,000}{500} \times 10^6$ = 6 × 10$^{-5}$ m$^2$
(Note: 30 000 and not 20 000 to allow for the 50% safety margin.)
Therefore each cable must have a cross-sectional area of 1.5 × 10$^{-5}$ m$^2$.
1.5 × 10$^{-5}$ = $\pi$d$^2$/4
$d$ = 4.3 × 10$^{-3}$ m = 4.3 mm

26 additional energy = $\frac{1}{2}F\Delta L = 0.5 \times 70 \times 10^{-3} = 0.35\,\text{J}$

27 (a) $L = 0.1\,\text{m}$

$e = \frac{FL}{EA} = 0.05\,\text{m}$

energy = $\frac{1}{2}Fe = \frac{1}{2}Eae^2/L$

$= \frac{1}{2}(5 \times 10^8 \times 1 \times 10^{-6} \times 0.05^2)/0.5 = 6.25\,\text{J}$

(b) $\frac{1}{2}mv^2 = 6.25\ v = \sqrt{\frac{2 \times 6.25}{5 \times 10^{-3}}} = 50\,\text{m s}^{-1}$

(c) $v^2 = u^2 + 2as$

$50^2 = 2 \times 9.81 \times s$

$s = \frac{2500}{19.62} = 127\,\text{m}$

28 extension $(e) = \frac{FL}{EA}$

$= \frac{70 \times 9.81 \times 0.4 \times 5}{1.8 \times 1010 \times \pi \times (10^{-2})^2}$

$= 2.42 \times 10^{-4}\,\text{m} = 0.242\,\text{mm}$

29 stress $= \frac{\text{force}}{\text{area}} = \frac{70 \times 9.8}{\pi \times (1.5 \times 10^{-2})^2} = \frac{686}{7.068} \times 10^{-4}$

$= 9.70 \times 10^5\,\text{Pa}$

## Chapter 5

1 (a) current $= \frac{20}{5} = 5\,\text{A}$

(b) $\frac{600}{20 \times 60} = 0.5\,\text{A}$

2 (a) charge $= It = 2 \times 10 = 20\,\text{C}$

(b) charge $= 5 \times 10^{-3} \times 8 \times 60 = 2.4\,\text{C}$

3 (a) $I = \frac{V}{R} = \frac{0.2}{120} = 1.7\,\text{mA}$

(b) $I = \frac{12}{4700} = 2.55\,\text{mA}$

(c) $I = \frac{6}{10^4} = 0.6\,\text{mA}$

(d) $I = \frac{25}{2.5} \times 10^6 = 10\,\mu\text{A}$

4 (a) $R = V/I = 12/0.25 = 48\,\Omega$

(b) $R = 230/10 = 23\,\Omega$

5 $\rho = RA/L = (3 \times \pi \times (0.28 \times 10^{-3})^2)/2.5$

$= 2.96 \times 10^{-7}\,\Omega\,\text{m}$

6 $R = \rho L/A = 0.65 \times 10^{-3}/1.5 \times 10^{-6} = 433\,\Omega$

7 When it is switched on due to the sudden expansion which gives the wire a 'thermal shock'.

8 (a) $200 + 400 = 600\,\Omega$

(b) $\frac{1}{R} = \frac{1}{400} + \frac{1}{200} = 0.0075\ R = 133\,\Omega$

(c) $R = \frac{750 \times 450}{750 + 450} = 281\,\Omega$

(d) $\frac{1}{R} = \frac{1}{500} + \frac{1}{500} + \frac{1}{500}$

$R = 167\,\Omega$

(e) $R = \frac{250 \times 200}{250 + 200} + 100 = 211\,\Omega$

(f) $\frac{1}{R} = \frac{1}{600} + \frac{1}{150} + \frac{1}{1200} = 109\,\Omega$

9 (a) $R = 50\,\text{k}\Omega$

Therefore:

$I = \frac{V}{R} = \frac{6}{50} \times 10^3 = 0.12\,\text{mA}$

(b) The resistance of the LDR will increase and so the current flowing from the cell will decrease.

(c) $I = \frac{6}{100} \times 10^3 = 0.06\,\text{mA}$ when the resistance of the LDR is infinite or when it is disconnected from the circuit.

10 (a) $V = 6\,\text{V}$

$I = \frac{6}{200} = 0.03\,\text{A}$

(b) $I = \frac{12}{200} = 0.06\,\text{A}$

11 (a) energy $= 1.5 \times 3000 = 4500\,\text{J}$

(b) energy $= 1.5 \times 200 \times 10^{-6} \times 2.5 \times 3600 = 2.7\,\text{J}$

12 energy $= 12 \times 200 \times 1.5 = 3600\,\text{J}$

13 power $= \frac{V^2}{R} = \frac{230^2}{50} = 1.058\,\text{kW}$

14 power loss $= I^2R = 4.5^2 \times 0.13 \times 0.75$

$= 1.97\,\text{W}$

15 (a) $I_3 = 0.096\,\text{A}$ flowing clockwise

(b) $E$ is as shown

$E = (0.096 \times 150) - (0.04 \times 100) = 10.4\,\text{V}$

16 (a) $I_3 = 0.3\,\text{A}$ flowing anticlockwise. $E$ must be reversed.

(b) $I_3 = 0.3\,\text{A}$ flowing clockwise. $E$ is as shown.

17 $V_2 = \frac{R_2}{R_1 + R_2} \times V$

(a) $V_2 = \frac{200}{300} \times 12 = 8\,\text{V}$

(b) $V_2 = \frac{20}{45} \times 10 = 4.4\,\text{V}$

(c) $V_2 = \frac{200}{450} \times 6 = 2.7\,\text{V}$

18 (a) The output p.d. will fall.

(b) The output p.d. will rise.

19 The output p.d will fall due to the greater loss of energy within the cell due to the greater current flowing through its internal resistance.

20  The voltmeter has such a high resistance that when the voltmeter is connected to the cell on its own only 1.3/10 MΩ = 1.3 × 10⁻⁷ A = 0.13 μA flows in the circuit.

The difference in the readings is because when the 20 Ω resistor is connected more current flows from the cell and so much more energy is lost within the internal resistance.

(a) current in the external resistor = $\dfrac{1.25}{20}$ = 0.0625 A

(b) Using $E = V + Ir$:

$1.3 = 1.25 + 0.0625r$

$\dfrac{1.3 - 1.25}{0.0625} = r$

internal resistance, $r = 0.8\,\Omega$

21  (a) (i) $I = \dfrac{E}{R + r}$

$I = \dfrac{2.5}{20.15} = 0.12\,\text{A}$

(ii) potential difference across the terminals = $IR$ = 0.12 × 20 = 2.48 V

(iii) power loss within the cell = $I^2r$ = 0.0154 × 0.15 = 0.0023 W

(b) (i) $I = \dfrac{E}{R + r}$

$I = \dfrac{2.5}{1.15} = 2.17\,\text{A}$

(ii) potential difference across the terminals = $IR$ = 2.18 × 1 = 2.17 A

(iii) power loss within the cell = $I^2r$ = 4.73 × 0.15 = 0.71 W

# Quantities units and symbols

| Quantity | Unit | Symbol |
|---|---|---|
| amount of substance | mole | mol |
| atomic mass unit | u | u |
| electric charge | coulomb | C |
| electric potential difference | volt | V |
| electromotive force | volt | V |
| electric current | | |
| electric resistance | ohm | $\Omega$ |
| resistivity | Ohm-metre | $\Omega$m |
| force | Newton | N |
| frequency | hertz | Hz |
| gravitational field strength | N kg$^{-1}$ | |

| Quantity | Unit | Symbol |
|---|---|---|
| length | metre | m |
| mass | kilogram | kg |
| moment of a force torque | Nm | M |
| momentum | Ns | P |
| power | watt | W |
| pressure and stress | pascal | Pa |
| thermodynamic temperature | kelvin | K |
| time | second | s |
| work, energy | joule | J |
| Young modulus | E | Pa |
| | | |

# Useful formulae

| | |
|---|---|
| Accelerated motion: $a = \dfrac{\text{change in speed}}{\text{time taken}}$ <br> $v = u + at \quad s = ut + \frac{1}{2}at^2 \quad v^2 = u^2 + 2as$ | Pressure $= \dfrac{\text{Force}}{\text{Area}}$ |
| Density $(\rho) = \dfrac{\text{mass}}{\text{volume}}$ | Refractive index $(n) = \dfrac{\sin i}{\sin r} = \dfrac{c_1}{c_2}$ |
| Diffraction grating maximum: $n\lambda = d \sin \theta$ | Resistance $= \dfrac{\text{voltage}}{\text{current}} = \dfrac{V}{I}$ |
| Double slit interference maximum: Fringe width $(w) = \dfrac{\lambda D}{s}$ | Resistivity $(\rho) = \dfrac{RA}{L}$ |
| Current $(I) = \dfrac{\text{charge}}{\text{time}} = \dfrac{\Delta Q}{\Delta t}$ | $\dfrac{1}{R} = \dfrac{1}{R_1} + \dfrac{1}{R_2} + \dfrac{1}{R_3}$ etc. |
| Electrical energy $= VIt$ | $R = R_1 + R_2 + R_3$ etc. |
| Energy $(E)$ = Planck's constant $(h)$ x frequency | Strain: $\dfrac{\text{Extension}}{\text{Original length } (\varepsilon)}$ |
| Force $= ma$ | Stress: $\dfrac{\text{Force}}{\text{Area } (\sigma)}$ |
| Gravitational potential energy $= mg\Delta h$ | Torque = Force x distance between forces |
| Kinetic energy $= \frac{1}{2}mv^2$ | Uniform velocity: <br> Speed $= \dfrac{\text{distance}}{\text{time}} \quad s = vt$ |
| Moment = Force x perpendicular distance from pivot | Wavelength of particle $(\lambda) = \dfrac{h}{mv}$ |
| Momentum = mass x velocity | Wave speed = frequency x wavelength |
| Photoelectric effect: $hf = \Phi + \frac{1}{2}mv^2$ | Weight $= mg$ |
| Potential difference $= \dfrac{W}{Q} = \dfrac{\text{energy}}{\text{charge}} = \dfrac{\text{Power}}{I}$ | Work = Force x distance |
| Power $= \dfrac{\text{Work}}{\text{Time}} =$ Force x velocity | Young modulus $= \dfrac{\text{Stress}}{\text{Strain}} = \dfrac{FL}{A\Delta L}$ |
| Power (electrical) $= VI = \dfrac{V^2}{R} = I^2R$ | |